JERSEY

The Hidden Histories

Paul Darroch

SEAFLOWER BOOKS

Published in 2015
and reprinted in 2017, 2019 and 2022 by
SEAFLOWER BOOKS

www.ex-librisbooks.co.uk

Origination by Seaflower Books

Printed by CPI Antony Rowe
Chippenham, Wiltshire

ISBN 978-1-906641-83-2

Dedicated to I, J and K

Front cover: The Death of Major Peirson, 6 January 1781 (detail) (1783)
John Singleton Copley 1738-1815
(Purchased 1864)
© Tate, London 2015

Contents

Prelude: The Day of the Aviators

Jersey, August 26, 1912

The clouds methought would open, and show riches
Ready to drop upon me; that, when I waked,
I cried to dream again.

Shakespeare, *The Tempest*

The Jersey Girl's Story: Miss Adderson

Hydro-Aeroplane Races, St Aubin's Bay
August 26, 1912

History is breaking in. It explodes over the Jersey skies with the force of an electrical storm. At first we scarcely notice the harbinger on the horizon, swooping in like a seabird over the waters. Then the black machine draws steadily, stealthily closer, and as it looms ever larger, the vast crowds below shiver in anticipation.

Suddenly we hear it – the sound of electric birdsong, an ethereal, unearthly hum droning high above the bay. As the sleek aircraft blazes in over the heights of Fort Regent, even the hard-bitten soldiers manning the battlements raise a primal, thunderous cheer. The terrible machine now soars overhead into full view, singing with a power undreamed of, gleaming with a fabulous technology that has effortlessly mastered the skies. The sight electrifies the human chain along the Esplanade, shocking us into a frenzied wave of delirium. We run headlong for the beach.

Then the first Aviator swoops down from heaven like an angel. He is a birdman in an elaborate cage, strapped like a moth to his fragile and beautiful wings. His hood and goggles surely mark him out as the high priest of a new age, an apostle of the world to come. His flying machine glides as sublimely as a swan over the choppy waters of St Aubin's Bay, finally coming to rest on the bridge right in front of the ancient castle. For a moment, the crowd is struck dumb by the impact. Then a fresh wave of hysteria ripples over us like wildfire, and we surge forward to embrace our glorious shining future. The very first aeroplane has arrived in Jersey. The power and glory of our sparkling new twentieth century has landed.

I have been dreaming of the Aviators for weeks. They loom in my mind as mythical heroes, god-men, casting off the iron chains that have kept us earthbound since the dawn of time. When I was a little child, my heart leaped at the first astounding wire reports out of North Carolina, and the first photographs of that heavier-than-air machine burning through the skies like a comet. If God had wanted men to fly, the scoffers said, He would have given us wings. Then one day, He did.

How I admire their daring feats of reckless courage! These are not the tamed, diminished men who shuffle ledgers in St Helier offices, whose light has been snuffed out under the crushing mediocrity of the daily grind. These are real men – heroes of old, ready to risk life itself for a fleeting second of glory. These knights of our age shine like Roman candles, lighting up the horizon in their breathless yet fleeting beauty. They scream across the heavens like bright meteors, burning all the more brightly because their time is so short. "Sacrifices must be made", cried the famous aviator Lilienthal as he lay dying after his glider plunged fifty feet to the ground. But who would not choose a week in flight as a glorious butterfly over a sad and sluggish lifetime as a caterpillar?

The fever gripped us today at the crack of the summer dawn. Vast crowds have been gathering along the bay since half past seven, amassing from the Albert Pier all the way to First Tower and beyond to Beaumont. A constant stream of motor traps and landaus jams the Avenue. The wet beach beyond the railway track is swarming with people, as heaving and black as a turgid mass of ants in the summer rain. It is as if the Island has been tipped on its axis, and all the people have tumbled like pebbles down the slope into the bay.

Farmers from Trinity have wheeled their wagons on the sand, still loaded with potatoes and bound for the Esplanade. Their horses whinny and stir restlessly, unnerved by the murmuring and expectant crowd. Mothers hoist babies aloft for a better view. Wizened old ladies whisper and scold in Jersey French. The babble and banter of the expectant crowd surges around me like the outgoing tide.

Then a dog barks an urgent, heartfelt warning. Suddenly we are all silent, eyes transfixed on the horizon. At first the object of our heart's desire seems no more than a lone gull dancing far away over the waters, or perhaps a child's lost kite twisting away over the sea. Then the black speck moves relentlessly closer, making for the shore. It travels towards us in a direct line far more precise and purposeful than any swooping gull. This is not a work of God, but of Man. It is the spearhead of a little flotilla. As the first incredible machine approaches the Fort, the air starts to throb with an eerie, exultant whine. I conjure a strange thought and revel in its novelty - I am listening to a choir of electric angels.

As the first astounding flying machine lands, there is a palpable gasp. My mind breaks free of its moorings and soars into spinning imagination. Let the kaleidoscope turn! I am a girl collecting seashells on the shores of Hispaniola when the first Spanish galleon breaks like a dark cloud over the vast and empty horizon. I am gathering flowers by Botany Bay when the alien hulk of HMS *Endeavour* heaves into view round the headland. Here in Jersey, the dark sea has always been our protector, both our comforting defence and our prison wall. We have been imprisoned in a beautiful looking glass since time immemorial. Today the glass has shattered in a single moment. Perhaps we will spend the rest of our lives chasing after the fragments.

A vast tremor of wild joy ripples right across the crowd. Sober and distinguished men are yelling like hoodlums. Granite-faced Jersey grandmothers are shaking their black umbrellas in celebration. The apple has fallen from the tree. We all feel released, for a few intoxicating moments, from the manacles of our commonplace lives.

A few girls are already plunging into the brine, determined to embrace their heroes, shrieking as if they have seen a ghost. They have hitched their skirts in a quite unladylike way, and are getting drenched by chilly waves for their pains. They really don't look the aquatic type, and their mermaid impression appears more ridiculous than romantic. I am a rather more practical girl. I think the Aviators deserve a nice hot jug of coffee.

So I dart back into our family kitchen at Bay View Terrace, and carry out a tray of hastily brewed Camp Coffee, laced with fresh and creamy Jersey milk. The crowds have not yet caught up with the pace of events on the western side of the bay– a third craft is landing just now near St Aubin – and they still seem mesmerised by the first plane on the Castle Bridge. So I dash over to the lonely second aeroplane on the dry sand near First Tower and blushingly present my gifts to the Aviators.

As I approach, my nostrils are filled with the curious stench of camphor oil and motor spirit. These gracious butterflies of the air harbour a guilty secret – at close quarters, they reek like a mechanic's workshop. The pilot leaps down to greet me, kissing my hand with his freezing blue lips. He is a swarthy, bright-eyed Frenchman, and he introduces himself as Michel-Paul Molla. His hair is flecked with shards of ice. He wolfs down the hot coffee in a moment and I peer hard into the inner sanctum of this temple of science.

These aeroplanes seem such flimsy contraptions, so wafer-thin and delicate that a mere gust might rip them to shreds. I run a hand over the wing, slimy with thick grease, and shiver at the frosting of ice. The chattering Aviators are absorbed in calibrations, fretting about fuel, barely noticing my presence. Still, they all seem delighted and most grateful for the coffee, even though I am quite sure it is not up to their refined Continental standards. Monsieur Molla kisses me a fond farewell, and I bound down from the plane like a gazelle.

A fourth plane has landed while I have been dallying. Heart pounding with the memory of my own boldness, I scurry back across the sands, just before the great swell of Jersey onlookers rushes up the beach. I grab Papa's prism binoculars and survey the scene unfolding over at the Castle Bridge. I can just make out the name *Sanchez-Besa* inscribed on the biplane, so according to the roster listed in the Evening Post, a Monsieur Jean Benoist must be the pilot. All really does not seem well up there. The tide is receding fast now and a surge of frenzied spectators is splashing and stampeding up to the hydroplane. The pilots are crying out for motor spirit, but the launch that supplies it seems to be delayed; someone has blundered.

They are losing valuable time, and their rivals are preparing to fly.

The crowds are flocking like a pack of scavenging crows, all seemingly desperate to touch the Aviators as if they are ancient kings who could cure scrofula. Some young men seem determined to steal souvenirs from the plane or even scratch their names as graffiti on the wings. The mood is turning ugly. The dutiful old parish Centenier is clearly struggling to hold back the mob, as the refuelling proceeds at a snail's pace. The airmen are howling with frustration, as they are set to lose the race before nightfall due to the delay. In desperation, the Aviators are hurling nuts and bolts at the crowd, which is fast mutating into a baying mob.

Suddenly the propellers whirr into life again as Benoist and his men prepare for take-off. Even as the lethal blades whir inches from their faces, the crowd refuses to back down. Eventually, the gallant Honoraries clear a space, and the hysteria that has gripped the crowd subsides in the face of the threat of harsh parochial discipline. The other hydroplanes have long fled. At last, Monsieur Benoist's beautiful biplane soars up like a swan into the heavens, freed from the heavy shackles of the earth. The little craft fades away into the sinking sun. The Jersey Aviators have flown at last.

The skies are silent, but my heart is hammering. I feel as if our sea-bound prison has suddenly been sprung open, our bleak and isolated centuries brushed away by the gossamer wings of a single brilliant butterfly. I stagger home, intoxicated by the splendour of all the sights my eyes have seen.

It has truly been a summer of miracles. August 1912 has scattered around me in a blaze of rainbows and scurrying showers. The kaleidoscope of time is turning fast now, as dizzying and beguiling as our young twentieth century itself.

The last days of summer are flashing by as fast as the stations on a Jersey Railway, racing towards a future bright beyond compare. I revelled in the splendid floats on Battle Day, in the Water Carnival and the dashing motorcycle races. How I laughed in uproar at the *Mumming Birds* when the Inebriated Swell (I think his name was Chaplin?) tumbled down from his balcony at the Opera House. I thrilled to the weekly cinema shows at West's Picture House and the dazzling electric light displays that glistened like jewels at Samarès Manor. All the golden days are cascading past in my imagination like a conjurer's deck of cards. Where will this dizzying parade end?

Night is falling fast now over the bay. The crowds have long vanished like a shallow summer mist. I am alone again. I peer out through the glass, watching a child's kite twist and tumble over the lonely sands, racing out to sea. I am suddenly exhausted by the shock of the new, the harbingers of this age to come. My thoughts seek refuge in the ancient and the familiar; the vastness of the bay, the burning sunset and the eternal, churning tides. I think back again to the deep past, to all those harried and eventful centuries that have lapped up against the bay and left only accumulating sand.

Who were the men and women who lived and died in Jersey, of whom we know nothing? When young King Charles sheltered in this castle so long ago, what would he have seen? Who stood watch on this very beach hundreds of years ago in the fierce medieval night, when French armies ransacked the island? What would my eyes have witnessed here some twelve centuries past, when Saint Helier skulked among the sea-rocks like a silent wraith? Who again might yet wander here in a hundred years' time, in some future world as remote and fantastical as to be beyond our wildest imaginings?

My eyes are already growing heavy in the drowsy warmth of the Jersey evening and so I begin to dream. What stories could our Island tell, if only she had the will to speak? What secret histories are buried forever in this prison of granite, only waiting to be given their voice? I stand ready to prise open the stories of Jersey from beneath the heavy rock, to listen to the cries of the waves as they shriek in over St Aubin's Bay.

They say that when the listener is ready, then the storyteller will appear. Jersey is my closest friend and she has walked with me all my days. She holds me close as I fall into sleep in the soft bosom of St Aubin's Bay. And as I drift away into the oblivion of night, she leans forward and begins to whisper her hidden histories to me.

EPISODE 1

The Rising Tide

Jersey Peninsula – 5,000 BC

The Hunter's Story: The Great Rock

The Great Rock looms as black as death on the horizon. It hollows out the sun and burns in our dreams. It marks the very edge of the world, where the continent itself shears off into the raging abyss beyond. No man has yet scaled its heights. Yet we are a desperate people, scattered by the force of the encroaching flood, and we have travelled west to claim it for our own.

The Rock glowers over the river plain like a vulture, feasting on the fiery bones of the western sunset. Nightfall is sweeping in fast now, swamping our little band of hunters as surely as the savagely rising tides. The last embers of our campfire fade away into dust. Then the stars wheel across the heavens, and the Rock swallows them up one by one, eclipsing each one in the consuming darkness of its shadow.

At daybreak we trek ever closer. To reach its easterly slopes by land, we must pick our way west over a desolate and waterlogged marsh. We struggle on through the treachery of quicksand, past the eerie night terrors of the ghostly marsh fires. We are following the hunting trails of a dying, drowning world.

The Rock towers higher than ever above us now, a god's fist angrily smiting the floodplain. Its stone faces hang like folds of skin above us, as pink and raw as a fresh birth. In these last days, the gods have poured out their hatred like hail, and our precious earth is flooding fast as their judgment falls. The western ocean screeches higher with each spring tide, sweeping away our old hunting trails, scattering all our sacred stones. All the rivers of the North have merged now into one furious, hellish channel, pulsing with vicious, icy melt-water. The heartland has been severed. The homeland has been drowned. Across the Great Divide, our kinsfolk still shriek for mercy from their watery graves.

So we have marched up to this last and highest place, this borderland between ice and rock, on the edge of our sinking continent. We come to plead before the gods of fire and ice, to snatch the spirits of our forefathers from the vulture's claw. We have skulked in the Rock's foothills for days, picking our way stealthily through the perilous marshes. We have dreamed of scaling its heights, surveying the earth like the fabled giants of old and raising strong stones of sacrifice. The Rock summons us deep into the caress of its shadow, and we glide like eels across the marshy plain.

The crest of the red Rock is fringed with thick pine forest, and it slopes upwards to the north, defying the watery abyss beyond. Down here, marsh-fires shimmer in thick mud, and the waterlogged plains throng with new life. The land all about us is flooding heavier by the week, but still it revels in its short season in the sun. A swarm of merciless tundra flies spin in a black and swirling cloud about our heads.

At daybreak, the sacred auspices are read. Our priests have carved up a brace of birds and their dissected entrails have ordained our fate. We must seize the highlands, or we will die. I knew in my heart this prophecy would come to pass.

As dawn breaks, we scale a heavily wooded hillside set about halfway across the muddy plain. If the spirits of the ocean do not relent, perhaps even these heights will soon perch like mere pebbles above the flood. Then we leap down into the final obstacle: a violent and churning river channel.

The torrent stings us, saps us, rips at our chests with the fury of a cornered wildcat, but our will is strong and we are fated to endure. Swimming up through the ice water, we lose our bearskins, shed our sins and scream our stories. We rage at the pain, and we find a way. Hauling ourselves like mangled seals onto the dry riverbank, we kiss the fresh grassland that we have won. On the other side, the land is gentle and it runs rich with game. The earth is breeding in a sheer frenzy now the spell of eternal winter has been broken.

We are home. The slope steepens and we scramble through tangled forest and a scraggy sea of boulders, the last residue of the ice age that has fled. Our grandfathers remembered the old ice world; our grandchildren will hear only the legends. Here we have found shelter and safe haven. Here we can bask in the power and comfort of the commanding heights.

Now we are become the vulture. We own the horizon. The land we have passed over falls away below us. We see the world through the eyes of a bird of prey; the sluggish snaking rivers, the slumbering hills perched halfway across the plain, and the immense embracing arm of the eastern highlands. To the north, the river we just crossed swells up to forge a cold, clear blue channel, before plunging into the Great

Divide. These fresh waters are already cutting us apart from the sister peaks to the north, now newly fledged islands carved by the power of the flood. Their destinies, it seems, will follow a different path.

We love our new and savage land, perched on this precipice between raging sea and deep woods, the abiding memory of bleak ice and the tantalising hope of a warmer, gentler world. Our first night here is spent nestled under trees on a wooded mountain crag that towers over the oxbow plain. It is a natural defensive outcrop, so our leader tells us. So we light a fire on the lonely hillside and our songs and war cries tumble deep down into the empty, drowning darkness below.

That night our shaman has a strange and fleeting vision. One day in this very place, in a distant and dying world, he declares that a great stone fortress will stand here. It will be named Mount Pride. It seems a good omen. So we sleep and watch and dream, nestling together under the wild stars.

An Island is Formed

*T*he world is changing. The Dreamtime is coming to an end. Our little band of hunter-gatherers does not know it, but the golden age of early man is drawing to a close. The last land bridge from Asia to Alaska has long since fallen beneath the waves. The era when hunters could stride boldly across the lost southern supercontinents of Sahul and Sunda is already fading into the abyss of unrecorded time. The wild joy of the hunt, the simple freedom of the nomad's life, will soon be forgotten. Ahead lies a world of toil and the serpent's curse, the sweat of the farmer's brow.

Long ago, the rising oceans roared back from the Western Approaches, fuelled by glacial melt-water, to progressively swallow up the Channel River and its lowlands. Britain clung to the continent only by the diminishing thread of its North Sea land bridge. Then a thousand years before our little hunter band reached Jersey, the coup de grace fell. An underwater landslide off Norway unleashed a vast tsunami, sweeping down from the north in a final cataclysm. Great Britain was newly born, severed from its mother continent, cut off by an icy sea. The melting of the polar ice cap had now entered its terminal phase. The scale and pace of the oncoming inundation scalped Guernsey, Sark and Alderney from the receding continent. The

Jersey peninsula remained, but the relentless rise of the waves would not spare it for long.

Many Jersey legends are tied to a primeval folk memory of this fearsome, surging sea. Our Iron Age ancestors certainly tilled vast fertile plains that are now long buried beneath the waves, resurfacing only as miles of bleak moonscape at the lowest tides. Some say that vestiges of the old lowlands managed to cling on for centuries. How else to explain the eerie tale of the sixth century Bishop of Coutances, who is reputed to have laid down a wooden plank across the marshlands to visit his faithful flock on the Ecréhous? Other storytellers recall the medieval revelry at the Jersey manor of La Brecquette, which lay swathed in deep woodland in St Ouen's parish. Then in one shrieking, catastrophic night in the fourteenth century, the chronicle records that a wall of water smashed down over its ramparts, and the ocean tore up the house without trace.

On neighbouring shores, we hear tantalising tales of the drowned forest of Scissy, where kings once hunted stags around the forest crag of Mont St Michel. Historians also note that the Romans referred to the Scilly Isles in the singular, and that ancient field walls run through submerged valleys. And back in Jersey, the scrolls at the very least suggest that the scraps of rock known as Green Island and the Ecréhous once boasted substantial meadows. The coastline, apparently as old as the hills, turns out to be something profoundly new – shifting, evolving, flooding and silting across the centuries, almost like a living thing.

Myth and history blend and merge, and we will never truly know the difference. But as the waters rose again, this time with powerful and decisive finality, new and strange settlers approached the land. Freshly ruptured from the continent, the Island of Jersey had been born, and it would have new masters.

So the old hunter-gatherers faded away into the mists of time, as if they had never been. A new civilisation was coming, a people far more cunning and skilled than their ancestors. These new men ploughed the rich soil of the newly minted Island. They left no history, no writing, and no songs. Their names died with them. Yet they carved their voices in stone. Their intricate granite circles shine under the cold moons, their labyrinths still keep silent watch over lonely hills. This was the time of the dolmen builders, and if you seek their monument, it surrounds us.

First, these strangers battered the land into submission. The new tribes massed in the vast primeval forests of Jersey, amidst the labyrinth of pillars of alder and oak that had flourished there from time immemorial, ever since the first passing of the ice. The aliens lit fires and gathered in massed ranks, chanting to new and foreign gods.

Then the world was put to the axe. The newcomers worked methodically, relentlessly, with communally organised diligence, to slash and burn the land. When the screeching forest giants had been felled, the ground was ferociously broken. Fierce pigs, strong boars with feral tusks, were unleashed to claw and dig out the roots and crush the remnants of vegetation. The heavy duty done, flocks of sheep were herded onto the land. Ravenous and persistent, they scoured the old forest floor like razors.

Now Abel kept flocks, and Cain worked the soil. The newcomers brought precious seed-corn, which swiftly flourished in the fertile fields. The first seedtime and harvest came and passed in the new land, and the flood did not cover them. With stone querns they eked out the surplus of the earth, extracting a rich bounty.

And so the Island was slowly tamed. On the great Rock, only vestiges of the old wild woods remained, in some thickly carpeted ravines and dark groves, where rivulets flowed fast towards the encroaching shoreline. Perhaps in these hollows, where waterfalls cascaded down the cliffs, the spirits of the ancient hunter tribes still lingered, flitting like shadows amidst the sea-caves.

The land had been savagely broken by human hand, but it soon flourished under their yoke. A Neolithic seafarer setting off in a crude bark from the Chaussey peninsula would have spied three newly tamed islands. Each one lay dappled with a patchwork of tilled fields and carved parcels of forest. The nearest was the wide, flat island we know as the Minquiers reef, long before it succumbed to the waves. The furthest was the newly severed Ecréhous, those mid-channel hilltops from which our original primeval hunters once surveyed their Promised Land. Within centuries, these too would be barren rocks. And the highest and greatest Island, boasting a long tail of fat farmland that stretched rich miles out to the future site of Seymour Tower, would one day be known as Jersey.

And on the commanding heights of this Island, Neolithic man chose to raise tremendous stone megaliths; at once elemental and savage, but as delicately honed as an axe blade. These monuments were built as a rite, an act of worship, the final act in the subjugation of the land. Hundreds toiled to raise them, to fuse the power of earth and fire and blood and leave a mark to last for the ages. Where once tall trees had towered, new stone beacons now stood watch, standing high above the surging sea.

The Shaman's Story: La Hougue Bie

All roads lead here. Like an intricate tattoo on a human face, our land is marked and mapped with tracks and ridges, lines and nodes. They mark territory, bind together the earth and create a shield against the power of the flood.

We built shrines to the gods of wind and lightning and earth, capping the highest crags, the loneliest peaks. A great stone circle crowns the mount above the southern bay. In the east, peering over the drowned floodplain, we built a new shrine to guard the eastern islands and survey the world from where we came. And everywhere we cast up the single, focal standing stones, the bleached white menhirs that harness and tame the secret spirits of the earth.

Our stones forge mere links in a vast chain, part of a great web of cairns and barrows and henges that girds the continent itself. From the wild shores of the mainland to the deep interior plains of the Great Island, our culture rings and brands the earth. We trade and barter with our brethren, giving breathtakingly beautiful ceremonial axes, whittled in honey-coloured jade, and receiving fine beakers in return. Stone and pottery, our mortal strength and beauty made enduring, are the pride and hallmark of our age. We bury them with our bones.

All roads lead here. For on this highest vantage point, the elders decreed that the greatest monument of all should be constructed, a tall mound visible from the farthest shore, a bold signal to the sea-gods that we have staked our undivided claim on this earth. The work took a generation. Great teams of strong men sourced stones from every corner of the land. From the far northern mountain, which peers over our craggy neighbours, our forefathers extracted and cajoled a great granite capstone. Another was prised from the great southern rock, the high solitary mount above the curving bay on the south side of the Island. The rocks were bound with strong rawhide rope and rolled on tracks of wood across the highlands. Bones were crushed and limbs were broken in the work. Sweat and blood dripped from us as we achingly set these rocks on high. Through our mortal sacrifice, we built eternity.

We have heard tell that on the mythical reaches of the known world, in distant and warmer lands, men are starting to raise ziggurats that reach up to the very heavens. This cairn is our own ladder to the gods. We built a home for our ancestors, to honour the wild lifeblood that courses in our veins. Their spirits scream on the violent winds, their shades linger under the woodland groves and their memory settles, gentle as a sea-mist, above the scorching fields in August. They need a home.

Then we gathered rocks and pebbles by the thousand from the new coasts, each one selected for its utmost purity. Each one was dedicated to bind the earth and protect it, each one a defensive wall against the rising sea-tide, the utter oblivion of death. We blessed the giant rocks of the great passage; we slaughtered lambs in the sanctuary; we buried all our memories in an immense cairn of stone. The entrance faces east, towards the mother continent, the old world of our forefathers. Flaming torches were placed at the door and the workers dismissed. Their work done, they slunk away to their old lives, to till and sow, to smelt and quarrel. No man was permitted to return. None dared.

I however am of the priestly caste, as my father and grandfather before me, draped in the dark arts of lightning and blood. On this black morning, one of the most sacred in our lunar calendar, I join them in the ceremony of the dawn. Just for an hour, the floodgates of the skies are thrown open. The warring factions and jostling clans throw down their feuds and we remember who we truly are.

The black and oppressive night is coming to an end. Outside, all the men, women and children are gathered in a throng, chanting and murmuring in a hypnotic rhythm. Their lifeblood pounds through our veins like exhilarating poison. They have grown demented on the juice of fermented grapes. They have feasted all night on great tranches of meat and wild honey, cereals and bread, the fruits of high summer.

Bonfires have been burning since nightfall, encircling the great dome of the cairn, raging wildly against the encroaching darkness. I watch the spirits of the ancestors whirling and leaping amidst their flames, aching to be free.

I retreat down the dark tunnel of the dead, towards the terminal cell. The voices of my ancestors are pounding in my head now, their stories and memories and deeds rattling like broken bones, screaming and scrambling for release. I stagger under the raw and chattering agony of their voices.

Revolution. Light begins to gently fall from heaven, the skies softening to indigo and blue. A gentle amber halo hovers above the far hills in the east. Then the fierce disc of the sun bursts like holy fire upon the Island. My forefathers, skilled in the arts of divining sun and moon, starlight and darkness, have calculated aright. This is the hour when day and night are in balance, where the summer and winter divide, splitting apart the past and future, the living and the dead.

Suddenly I am bathed in dazzling, radiant light. As the sunrise bursts upon us, I dance down the tunnel like a young and joyous foal. The black shrouded stone that has languished in darkness for a year suddenly bathes in a honeycomb of light.

The fever in my head is silent at last, the tumult of arms and voices stilled. My earthly brothers and sisters are slumped around the cairn, like felled trees, mad with wine, as if toppled by an unseen hand. I stride out of the tunnel, freshly born.

Somewhere far away, the spirits of my forefathers fall back into the nurturing and gentle earth, scattering softly like a quiver of summer grain.

A World Forgotten

*W*e do not know why the great stone cairn of La Hougue Bie was finally abandoned. Some say that there was a profound cultural change, when the sense of an open heaven, the daily conversation of the living and dead in the life of the tribe, came to an end. The barrow was sealed and covered in earth. A barrier had been definitively placed between the future and the past. The world moved from a unified tribal bond to a more stratified world of kings and subjects, rulers and ruled.

Over the centuries the ancient mound, the legacy of a lost world, became a place of myth and fable. All roads still converged on the site, from all directions, and it remained a mooting place, a vantage point and a natural refuge. But the old rites of worship had fled. The future belonged to foreign gods, to the earthly glory of Rome, the power of the lightning bolt and the wings of the eagle.

And when the new faith of the Nazarene exploded like an unstoppable fire across the world, the ancient cairn was pressed into the service of a new and living God. A chapel dominated its summit and the mound, now as soft and unassuming as a grassy hill, became a natural boundary to divide the new parishes. All over the Island, the old ways were co-opted, ancient pagan monuments consecrated as altars of worship.

Folk memories of the darker, older times lingered like the great sea mists that rolled in on deep winter nights. The ancient chronicles spoke of a great dragon that stalked the mound, which was slain by the brave Seigneur de Hambye. Yet a treacherous, jealous servant murdered the gallant knight in his bed. Now his armoured body lies entombed for eternity in this eerie sepulchre. He rests here, sword by his side, waiting for the thunderclap of Doomsday, for the light to finally burst through the tunnel of death and restore him to life.

And in the ages to come, Romantics would attempt to revive the mystery and melancholy of the ancient monument. The irrepressible and eccentric Philippe d'Auvergne, Duc de Bouillon, raised a flamboyant neo-Gothic folly on the site, a madcap masterpiece of towers, ramparts and spires. It was dubbed Prince's Tower.

Black-clad Victorian visitors would part with a farthing for the sheer delight of ascending the tower and surveying a panorama of the Island. The splendid vistas stretched out in every direction, the orchards as bucolic and well-tended as a pleasure garden. It seemed the dragon had at last been tamed, the primal power of the cairn subdued. The pagan necropolis had become a tourist trap for the leisured antiquarian.

Beneath it all, the white bones of the ancients rested, undisturbed. As the huddled and eventful centuries rolled by, the dark passageway of rock lay buried deep in the earth, and the sleepers did not awake. The sunrises of the vernal and autumnal equinox shone onto a grassy, abandoned hill, and the secret entrance remained sealed and forgotten. Blending into the landscape and fading into the realm of story, the great monument stood as a silent epitaph to a vanished world.

The barrow men had fled. The wheel of history turned.

Fire and Shadow

Jersey 50 BC – 1204 AD

An Empire Rises and Falls

*R*ome, a name to conjure with, a blazing imperial sun circled in fiery splendour over a vast continent, drawing even remote islands like tiny and distant asteroids into its orbit. From their lofty heights on the Imperial Capitol, the Emperors presided over an extraordinary pinnacle of human civilisation, yoking the shores of Europe, Africa and Asia Minor together to bask in their reflected glory. Absolute loyalty to Caesar Augustus yielded its own reward, bringing ample blessings of peace and trade, bread and circuses. Resistance of course led to utter annihilation, the extirpated civilisation perhaps meriting a footnote in the annals of one of the more scrupulous historians. Profitable homage or merciless extinction; it was an easy choice for a few simple island fishermen to make.

This chain of islands that the Roman chroniclers dubbed Riduna, Sarnia, Caesarea and Andium were at first little more than passing curiosities on a map. These scattered specks marked almost the furthest reaches of the known world. They were a handy navigational aid, at best a convenient port-of-call to supply ships with victuals as they plied the seas between Armorica and the tin ports of Britannia.

We can imagine the first impressions of a Roman citizen, thoroughbred and haughty, passing through en route to saddle and spur his subservient British domains. This newcomer, fresh from the breath-taking splendour of the Eternal City and the indulgent delights of the Baths of Caracalla, will find little to love here. The bleak Channel is a world removed from the excitement and bloody showmanship of the Flavian Amphitheatre, where crowds lapped up spectacles under the radiant *golden auspices of Nero's Colossus. How could the simple conger eel fishers on these rocks comprehend the sophistication and bounty of the Roman Forum? How could they conceive of the passion and energy of the heart-stopping Circus Maximus, where a hundred and fifty thousand spectators cheered and roared like thunder? Even to a son of Rome, born and bred, the glamour of the Palatine seems now like an impossibly distant dream, half a world away.*

Romans typically feared the sea, and the vicious tides and jabbering barbarians of these little rocks must have comprised a distinctly unappetising combination. Yet needs must, and money talked. So trade ships delivered rich cargos of Gaulish amphorae and fine wine. The boats hauled back bond slaves and Cornish tin. St Peter Port became a bustling hub, a thriving entrepôt of the isles. Curses were cast into the sea; Roman gods were worshipped, and coins bearing the shining image of a distant Emperor made his minions rich. The scattered detritus and lost property of the age has become its legacy; a mislaid Roman brooch at St Aubin, a coin hoard in a field; shards of pottery and memory buried deep beneath the earth. A simple temple, bathed in the Atlantic sunsets at the natural shrine of Le Pinacle, anchored heaven to earth, securing the islands in the warm favour of the Roman gods. Of course, history had other plans.

The long and bright Roman day was at last drawing to an end. The collapse of the Old Empire, in a downward spiral of decay and treachery and rebellion, took centuries to play out in all its gory drama. Then the borders broke and the foundations crumbled.

It was a sign of the times when the Imperial fleet garrisoned a great square stone naval fort at Alderney, placing a stake in the ground against the threat from the north. The naval squadron did its best to harry and deter the pirates, to control the narrow strait, to fight the rising tide. As night rushed in, history folded into legend. Eventually the imperial sun slipped below the horizon when the River Rhine was crossed, an act as fatal and decisive as Caesar breaching the Rubicon all those centuries before. As the barbarians surged in and settled, the Roman Empire had ceased, in a very real sense, to be their civilisation any more. It had become ours.

Gaul swiftly collapsed in a cascade of capitulation that did not end until the Imperial Forum itself burned in flames. Within a century, sheep were grazing amidst its broken ruins. As a heaving mass of barbarian tribes ransacked Rome, the fate of a few minute islands on the furthest reaches of the world mattered not a jot. The Imperial heights could never now be regained and the damage could never be undone. The ancient world haunts our dreams only as a lost idyll, a memory, something forever beyond reach. They say the owl of Minerva, the Roman goddess of wisdom, flies only at dusk. And perhaps only at the very end, as the libraries burned and the palaces crumbled, could the world begin to fathom what it had lost, when all lay beyond repair.

On northerly Riduna, the great Roman fort designed to harry and deter barbarian pirates fell into enemy hands; its elite naval fleet scuttled, its defences ravaged. The trading ships no longer flocked to St Peter Port laden with rich cargos for Britannia, bearing amphorae of wine north, hauling back British tin and slaves. The Islands, exposed and vulnerable, were left to their own fate. And when the end finally came, there was no one left to protect them.

Doubtless the islanders tilled their fields and plied their fishing boats, like their ancestors before them, as if nothing had changed. Things of course would never be the same. Night had fallen on Jersey and it would bring fire and slaughter in its wake.

The old order had fallen. New prophets would soon come calling on Jersey's abandoned shores.

The Disciple's Story: Saint Romard

6th Century AD

The first holy men came from the east, but they were never truly of this world. These lone warriors, the fierce advance guard of a new faith, first screamed their gospel across the barren desert of Scissy. Gaunt and ascetic, they shunned worldliness in every form, dressing in brown hooded robes and walking unafraid, without water, food or coin, wholly at the mercy of their God.

These pioneers thrived in the wilderness, lean and sunburned, proudly bearing the scars of their mortification. So lithe were their shrivelled frames, despite the perpetual burden of penance, that their very bodies seemed consumed by the fire of God. They carried the hot fervour of the Near East in their blood; the outward ripples of the fierce flame that had exploded in Jerusalem five centuries before.

My master Helier was such a man. He was the son of a wealthy Saxon count-governor, and hailed from the Roman frontier fortress of Tongeren. He could have chosen a life of ease and opulence, far from the icy rock-pools and bed of stone he eventually made his home.

As usual, it was the fault of the parents. Desperate for a son and heir, they had begged the wandering evangelist Cunibert for a miracle, promising their speculative, longed-for child to the service of God. They lied. So young Helier ran away from the pagan idolatry and barbarian money-lust of his parents to seek sanctuary with his spiritual father, Cunibert. Like the young Christ, he grew in faith and fervour. He ministered to the poor and sick of this old garrison town, poised on the edge of the civilised world and facing the eternal forestland beyond. Then he endured his own Calvary. He came home one day to stare death in the face, to see his beloved mentor murdered. His powerful and jealous parents had arranged this violent desecration.

So Helier fled. He staggered into the embrace of the great western forests and raced away for seven days, away from pain, away from the curse of Cain. He was on the run for the rest of his life, hurtling through the wilderness, treading the forgotten fringes of a violent and fragmented world. Heading west, spreading signs and wonders like scattered grain, Helier trekked to the coastal lands. Like Moses in the desert, he is said to have commanded water to pour from a barren rock. Tradition tells he purified a poisoned well in the village of Fruges, but the agony of his soul could not be so easily purged. So he devoted himself to penance, pain and mortification, to draw ever closer to the passion of his Christ.

And then on the wild crescent beaches of northern Gaul, where the great peninsula juts out like an arm to punch Britannia, he met Brother Marculf, a fellow pilgrim and tamer of the dark places of the world. These shadowy figures flit and slide around the fringes of the fire, and so little is known whenever myth and truth merge. I was just a young errand boy, a novice dashing round the monastery, beguiled by the sanctity and sadness of this strange and lonely wanderer. Sometimes my own memories seem as pale as dreams, as the whirl of faces and places is lost in the summer mist.

The age of the assiduous Roman chroniclers has long gone, and the world is again a place of mystery and rumour. It is a time when countless men and women live and die, and even of their kings, we know nothing. Yet a few men stepped forward into the darkness, the brief candles of their lives flickering for a moment in the blackness. Helier was such a man, and I chose to follow my master into the light.

I do not remember exactly when we first set foot amidst the pitiful huddle of fishermen's huts that clung to the bleak dunes of Jersey's southern shores. Their little village was perched on the edge of a foul and waterlogged marsh, where children would sometimes be sucked away into the treacherous rivulets during the flood tide. The villagers' stock-in-trade was conger eels; dried in the sun and salted before export. There is no harbour here, but the deep tides that scour the bay allow boats to beach on the foreshore, where I would one day found a church, and set sail twice daily for their haul. The town boasts as few as thirty dwellers, eking out a living between sand dunes and salt marsh, under the shadow of the red granite crag.

It did not take long for this ascetic, lean stranger, still clad in his desert robe, to make a stir. The first Islander we encountered was lame old Antequil, who habitually whiled away the days slouched on a boulder over the bay. He expected nothing more than another bitter and grieving morning, but the hinge of history was about to turn. The miraculous energy that the Apostle Peter had unleashed at the Beautiful Gate of Jerusalem had finally reached this scrappy, forgotten rock. My master Helier cried to the heavens: "Silver and gold I do not have, but in the name of Jesus Christ of Nazareth, walk!"

My eyes are old and blind now, but I remember that day as clear as noon. I saw Antequil leap into the air in joy, and the conversion of Jersey was sealed in an instant. The townsfolk were after all sullen and cowed men, scratching out a pittance, haunted by the fear of the seaborne lights, the dark threat of the Norse long-ships who came only to steal and kill and destroy. Their old gods had failed. They were ready for a new Gospel.

My master duly preached the word of Saint Matthew: "The axe is already at the root of the trees, and every tree that does not produce good fruit will be thrown into the fire". The Islanders knew all about axes, and all about fire. As Helier preached the prescient warning of John the Baptist to his eager audience, they remembered all too painfully the cataclysm that had overwhelmed them as surely as the storm waves at flood tide. Their magnificent Roman villas had long been consumed by sword and flame. Their ancient temple at Le Pinacle, poised in a site of soaring beauty over the surging Atlantic breakers, had lain empty for a century or more. The pagan shrine that had blazed with the fire of a hundred thousand sunsets had long since been plundered and burned. No matter. Those gods were not needed any more.

The raiders returned again and again to strike without warning, like a primeval force of nature from the north, and it seemed they could not be bargained with, paid off, or resisted. The only defence was to melt away into the thick *bocage* of the interior of the Island, seeking refuge in the *cotils* and hidden groves known only to local lore. Then, with the ferocity of the storm spent and their plunder seized, the pirates would retreat and the villagers could filter back, their spirits broken, to the charred remains of their hovels.

Helier decided to stand in the gap against the storm. He moved out to the tall pinnacle of rock that stood alone in the bay, making his home there amidst the gulls. A silent watchman, he stood alone against the sails of death, the curse on the far horizon. Many times he caught sight of the pirate hordes and signalled to me on the land, so I could shepherd the villagers away in safety to the high plateaux and hiding places of the Island.

False tongues said Helier was a ship-wrecker, luring the pirates to their doom by false lights and deceptive signs. In the rock-infested, newly drowned waters off Jersey, it was after all so easy for a foreign pilot to take a false channel, or miss a sudden reef that would lacerate his boat like plywood. Then the rich spoils would float in on the tide, like manna from heaven, and the fisher folk would celebrate the bounty of the wreckage for days. The sea could brutally steal and kill, but it could also yield a rich fruit. We dreamt and prayed and wept amongst the sands.

It was high summer when Christ took my master home. My failing memory recalls the date as the sixteenth of July, some five hundred and fifty five years since the census of Caesar Augustus in the province of Judea when, in a sense, his story first began. Doubters may question the suspiciously palindromic date, or even the very existence of this wizened, emaciated hermit who once skulked like a seal among these blackened sea-rocks.

Helier cares nothing for your dates or times or history; he is at one with the blood-red granite, the raw daily lashings of salt and spray and sun. Like an eel drying on the bare rock, he lets the sun scourge his flesh, till he is covered in mottled brown moles and scabs. Then, with a wail of holy delight, he leaps into icy rock-pools, feeling the chilly water soften and bloat his flesh, till it is purged and raw. Finally, as the sky begins to spin and the darkness in his head begins to explode, he hauls himself back to the stone bed he has found in the heights of the rock. He chunters and prays for hours, the words smashing like hammers and chisels in his mind, cutting away at the solid stone that encases him.

Despite my loving entreaties, Helier has not eaten for months. He has moved so far beyond the mortal plane that sweet is bitter and pain is joy. Helier's white bones jut out prominently from his thinly stretched tent of flesh. His dreams have become darker of late, and his strength is waning, like the pale moon at daybreak. Helier knows he will soon be going home.

On the vanishing point of the horizon, across the great divide where sea and sky meet, a flurry of dark clouds rushes inwards. The weather is changing. Helier stutters and prays, and through his murmurings he catches his breath. A cloud is bolder, blacker, growing. A sail.

The drill is well rehearsed. Yet it takes an age, agonisingly slow as spasms of pain convulse this husk of a man, but Helier lights a small fire in a pre-ordained hollow. The townsfolk see the signal and Helier sees them scurrying like flies, gathering their children, packing their precious dried eels and heading for the defensive ramparts deep inland, where the raiders might fear to tread. And as the sleek Viking ships draw into the great bay, they encounter a ghost town, with the cooking pots still warm, sheepskins drying on the line. This sad cluster of huts is barely worth a flaming torch, but the pirates provide one for tradition's sake. I stay, crouching in a hole in the sands, watching and waiting for my master.

The Northmen have witnessed the fire on the rock. Now they are determined to crush this shadowy rat, this slippery tale-teller, to butcher the trickster of false lights who has led so many of their kinsmen's ships to utter doom. So a raiding party in a low longboat draws up close to the hermit's rock. Black axes drawn, the soldier-pirates plunge waist-deep onto the slippery, treacherous reef, their chain mail jangling in the cold surf, their blood lust rising to fever pitch.

A shadow falls, a cry shrieks, and a prayer is whispered. The quarry is soon cornered, dragged by his thinning hair from his rock bed, as frail as a ghost. *Ecce homo.*

Helier prays with the boldness of a bounteous heaven. His eyes are half-blinded by the salt surf and the white mist of cataracts, the fruit of the dazzling bay. He sees bright angels descending and ascending above the Son of Man. So for the final time he prays a blessing, radiating the divine love that has burned in his heart since childhood, since far and distant Tongeren, when all the world was fresh and new.

The brute, wolfish men stagger and quiver as the message hits home, their hearts pierced by his beauty and courage. Yet their warlord baulks in rage, as his vaunted attack dogs falter. So in a rage, he crosses his double axes above his head, building the anger of the strike, pumping his veined muscles into a frenzy of raw and furious power.

Helier turns one last time to face his bed of stone, his gentle sea-garden. So great a cloud of witnesses surrounds him, and Cunibert smiles. Helier briefly feels the shadows of his parents, vainglorious, murderous yet driven by twisted love, hover on the summer breeze. They have come to say goodbye, for they know they cannot follow. The axes plunge down.

Gravity does its inevitable work, as Helier floats towards the consuming light. The dark glass shatters and for the first time, he sees face-to-face. Cherry-red blood throbs and pulses hard from his severed neck, his surprised heart spurting it out in spades over the red rock. Then falling as gently as a seagull's feather, or the soft sea mist rolling across the bay, my master slips into the shroud of myth and legend.

High above, the seabirds swivel and soar, unheeding. Then the tide turns once again to beat its remorseless pilgrimage, and the first clouds of sunset race in towards the sands.

A Dark Age

*T*he fisher folk did not forget their fallen saint. On the nearest point at the sandy shore, where the dunes and mudflats rise up and caress the solid ground, they built a little chapel to honour him. By the eleventh century, a stone church towered here, the beating heart of a thriving medieval port proudly named after Helier himself. In the adjacent square, a market flourished. And so this raw, salt-flecked saint, a man of wild and delirious visions, was frozen here in stained glass, memorialised in the exquisite beauty of his own shrine. The rock of his martyrdom also became a chapel, and nearby, on another scraggy islet in the bay, a great monastery was founded shortly after his bloody demise.

The new religion was here to stay. Under the auspices of the great Pretextatus, the exiled archbishop of Rouen, the Island was definitively anchored to the Frankish diocese of Coutances. Ancient pagan routes and natural watercourses were transformed into parish boundaries, as the holy men claimed the land. A carnival of saints paraded out of history to claim title to this remote rock. The litany begins with St Martin of Tours, the Roman soldier who cut his tunic in two to give succour to a poor beggar, who was revealed to be the living Christ. It continues with St Peter himself, crucified upside down before the baying crowds at Nero's Circus, his sepulchre by now the greatest Cathedral in all of Christendom.

Meanwhile St Clement took charge of the marshy southeast lands, which still flooded at equinoctial springtide. Shoring these defences was an apt task for the diligent 'fellow-labourer' commended by the Apostle Paul in his letter to the Philippians. The fierce north of the Island was placed under the holy care of St John the Baptist, the prophet whose severed head once graced Herod's platter. Meanwhile, the deep interior valleys were duly consecrated to poor St Lawrence, a man who had been cruelly cooked like raw meat on a Roman griddle. Passus est, recorded the unblinking hagiographer. He suffered.

Later still, the remote west fell under the alluring spell of the Breton saints. The southern portion was given to St Brelade, the wandering Celt who hailed from the ancient land of Tintagel and King Arthur, and travelled barefoot to evangelise the Cornish peninsula. He dutifully watched over a small sinner's chapel and parish church, nestled in the snug curve of a golden bay. Meanwhile a colourful Frankish bishop, St Ouen, lent his name to that thick muzzle of land in the northwest, which destiny had called to become Jersey's richest and most illustrious fief.

Eventually, a man stepped forward to claim the Imperial Crown of Rome, which had lain trampled in the dust for centuries. Anointed by the Pope, the great warrior Charlemagne briefly ruled over the revivified body of the western Empire. For one fleeting and flourishing moment, Europe was united. In gratitude, the emperor decreed that the tenth ear of corn should be consecrated to the Church, and thenceforth tithes flowed like new wine into the open coffers of the parishes. These riches funded the great stone parish churches, Jersey's enduring landmarks, each one cruciform and towering, carving up the land for the Lord.

History flowed and ebbed with the tides. The Vikings came as pagan plunderers but stayed to found a kingdom. The power of Helier's prayers must have lingered, for these Norse warlords became holy warriors, cathedral-builders, men of savage piety and sweet brutality. They slew mercilessly, and then endowed rich chantries for the purification of their souls. They wreaked havoc from York to Sicily, then as if to compensate conjured a phoenix, a new civilisation from the ashes.

And so the Islands were cast like dice into the hands of William Longsword, man of power, fierce commander of the Norsemen. His heirs became the Dukes of Normandy, and when one of them set sail for Hastings, the fate of entire nations hung in the balance. Of course, the arrow that flew at mid-day found its target and the flower of Anglo-Saxon chivalry succumbed to the power of the Norman sword. The triumphant Dukes became the Kings of England. And as the White Tower was raised over a subdued and compliant London, and the royal assessors of Domesday fanned out across an occupied land, little Jersey lay securely in the bosom of a new realm that spanned both Channel coasts.

Jersey thrived, from the region of Crapaudoit that lay across the toad-river in St Peter's Valley, over to the fledgling huts of Gorroic in the east. And when the Plantagenet Empire rolled out like a royal tapestry from Hadrian's Wall down to the mountain forts of the Pyrenees, trade ships again plied the lucrative sea routes from England to Aquitaine. These fortunate isles prospered.

In Jersey, the common people dried eels on the beach, just as they had done from time immemorial, and quarrelled and lusted and prayed. The Kingdom of Congers, they laughingly called their land. The monks cheerfully ground their corn in watermills over the brooks. The clergy genuflected to the bishop of Coutances, whose great new cathedral was rising like the dawn on the eastern horizon. Salt ships from Gascony moored at St Helier's Church, while ducal barges set sail for sea, shipping taxes of heavy coin over to the Exchequer at Caen.

The lepers languished in the leper-houses, clad in black and weeping in silence. The peasants toiled hard and tilled the land. The gallant seigneurs hunted hard and ruthlessly extracted their dues. Of an evening, they charmed themselves with the ballads and poetry of Jersey's most famous son, Master Wace, entertaining the fancy that their dull provincial lordships matched the romance of Camelot, *the chivalry of the Round Table, or the purity of the grail. Noblewomen devotedly pored over their books of hours, while the clergy assiduously counted their tithes. The times were as good as they could ever be, in the capricious and cruel medieval world. After 1203, even the barren rocks of the Ecréhous sprouted a little chapel, and a light shone on that lonely reef in the darkness, to guide lost souls home.*

Such were the fat and happy days. Such was peace in Jersey. It could not last.

EPISODE 3

The Siege

Jersey 1373

War and Plague

*W*ar. *It came to this island as surely as the lashing rain of winter, or the remorseless advance of the scourging tides.*

Men heard it in the dark whispers and oaths of Breton traders, mooring their barques by the seawall of the Town Church. They saw it in the thousand-yard stare of the Castle soldiers, in eyes that have seen men charred by Greek fire, and ravens feast on the flesh of fallen knights on a dozen battlefields.

Gone are the distant years when Jersey nestled like a baby within the protective embrace of both England and Normandy, loyal and secure under one dynasty. King John Lackland put paid to all that. In the winter of 1204, the great Plantagenet fortress of Château Gaillard fell to its titular overlord, the French King. They dubbed this foreign conqueror Philip Augustus in honour of his military prowess, and the Imperial title fitted well. The Seine valley – the very ancestral homeland of Normandy – folded before him like a pack of cards. The great abbey of Fontevraud, the hallowed resting place of the Plantagenet kings, fell into his hands. Good King Richard could scarcely have imagined that the banner of the white lilies, the pennant of his nemesis, the King of France, would soon enough fly high above his tomb.

The conniving, ambitious Jersey nobles naturally saw an opportunity with this turn of events. The local seigneurs pledged troth to the English King, thus elevating themselves to the status of tenants-in-chief, the better to wring new liberties and privileges from their weakened, desperate lord. They gained their cherished freedoms, but they paid for it with the lives of their sons. Bailiffs and Jurats won their titles, but were doomed to perch forever on the bloody frontier of clashing kingdoms.

Honour demanded its blood price, and in due course the bill was delivered. The oldest alive could scarcely remember a time before the war, which had become the fearsome hallmark of the age. Like the moon the conflict waxed and waned, and sometimes the angel of death skirted these rocky shores. For the age had spawned a new terror, the chevauchée, *the savage and sudden military strike, the shadow that swoops in the night without warning or mercy. The tactical aim was havoc and wanton destruction, and a swift escape by daybreak, the strategic goal to bequeath crippling fear, to break the spirit. The leaders of the Island were not of one mind, and with every loss, every burial, the French faction came a little closer to winning its case. So the dice of history were thrown, and the blood feuds between slippery and perfidious families turned the Island into a pit of vipers.*

The plague years were the worst. The islanders watched the corpses piling up for burial in great pits outside the stone church of St Helier. They grieved at the Chapel of Notre Dame de Pas, overlooking the rocks at Havre de Pas, but they knew in their hearts that peace had truly fled the island, and the light of Our Lady had grown dim. Her icon still wept over them in the chapel, crowned with celestial stars, but her grace seemed far from the bitter earth. And so the black-clad monks from the Abbey thronged like ravens among the graves, tending to their chantries in cold and pitiless Latin. It will not be long until the dead swell in number again. This time the means of suffering will not be plague, but slaughter.

The king of France is on the move again, staking his claim to these islands, flushed with the arrogant certainty of Salic law, his knights ready to sweep the English dogs from their feet. They are raising an army of ten thousand men in the south to lay siege to Brest.

Death is coming to these shores. Men sense it in the salt-tang on the sea breeze, and the blood moon that hangs like a harbinger over the walls of Gorey Castle. It bloats in the dark eyes of the lepers on the hill, it chatters in the beaks of the crows that haunt these battlements. The hammer is about to fall on Jersey. It will be soon.

The Knight's Story: Sir William Asthorpe

His name conjures sheer terror. Bertrand Du Guesclin, Constable of France, is a man with the genius of Hannibal, the strategic talent of Alexander, and the duplicity of Brutus.

Our priests tell us our faces reflect who we truly are, and he is said to be a squat and ugly toad. Mocked and scorned by the fairer sex, he has channelled his revenge upon other men through the black instruments of war. His ruthless concentration of power, his relentless harrying, his Fabian strategies of attrition, have ground kings and realms into the dust.

The Black Dog of Brocéliande grew up deep within Merlin's haunted forest in Brittany, the realm of fountains and magic that our own great poet Master Wace has immortalised in ballad. Du Guesclin must have learned his war-craft through black sorcery, in the bowels of Merlin's tomb. He is a self-made man, a lowborn cur from minor Breton stock, who has somehow tricked and conjured his way to the greatest office of state, Constable of France. Some say he wishes to be enshrined beside the French kings at Saint-Denis, cloaked like them in the glory of the lilies of France.

Du Guesclin is surely no chivalrous and courtly knight. The plague of his so-called free companies, mercenaries driven by lust for gold, terrorised the Spanish peninsula. He is a regicide, a king-slayer. They say he notoriously pinned down Pedro I of Castile so that the usurper Henry could stab him to death. His equivocal response – "I neither put nor remove a king, but I help my master" – is worthy of a Brutus or worse. Naturally he received his thirty pieces of silver, in the guise of a dukedom.

Enough of this chatter! The message arrived this morning at the Castle, by boat. Brest has agreed terms. My garrison is weak, my forces denuded and unprepared. We are a poor land. The long years of suffering have sapped the strength of the Island, and too many are ready to parley and prattle for peace.

I remain Sir William Asthorpe, the Warden of the Isles, appointed here by the royal command. I came to this front line, to guard these scraps of land, lured by the hope of glory and the promise of lordly revenues. Sometimes, as the cold light glitters on the bay, I remember the soft Devon hills where I was born and raised and feel the warmth of the roaring hearths of my ancestral home at Hemyock. It feels as far away as the distant stars that race in the blackness overhead. Now the war is in the marrow of my bones, in the dull monotony of sharpening swords, of straining to watch the sea channel until our eyes snag and blur on the horizon.

Now the wheel of fate has caught up with me. I will fight.

A Castle Falls

For the people of the island the news is shattering. Grosnez Castle has fallen. No great prize this, merely a crude bastion of stone and iron on Jersey's northern peninsula, perched on a grim grey headland, lurking high over the pounding waters. The French faced mere shepherds and peasants, scared witless and unfit for war, wielding rough halberds and pitchforks. The terrified locals corralled themselves within, believing they had found sanctuary. Holed up along with their rancid animals and mewling babies, they lacked both fresh water and supplies. They acted as if they were evading a gang of cattle-rustlers, or perhaps sheltering from a crew of Malouin corsairs.

In truth these blind peasants faced the elite field army of the King of France, commanded by the Duke of Bourbon himself. So they opened the gates. His gallant and lavishly armoured knights were it seems loath to make mincemeat of such pitiful specimens, so after they had punished the ringleaders, pour encourager les autres, *the French duke graciously accepted both their fealty and their worldly goods. How quickly the quaking flock betrayed their loyalty to the King of England! The point of a sword proved an artful and compelling persuader.*

Now the French are coming for the great castle of Gorey. Constable du Guesclin, whom men rate as the military genius par excellence of the age, is not renowned for his mercy.

The Knight's Story: A Castle Stands

So this is the theatre of war. The Island around us simmers in the dull and oppressive heat of a glorious July day. The sunlight shimmers and glistens off the splendidly aquamarine bay, and a few sea-gulls lark boisterously on the shoreline. The air is deep and still, steeped in a summer trance, as if a single kiss might break the spell. A thick pillar of black cloud, twirling with a strange beauty on the horizon, wafts languorously up to heaven. This fire is fuelled by wood and straw, the last testament of the blazing town houses of St Helier.

Jersey lies raw and pillaged. Eden is ravaged, and I have failed in my first duty as Warden of the Isles. The people have fled to the high points, melted into the hedgerows like vagabonds, or clumsily prostrated themselves before the short mercy of a new King. Fields of lush crops already lie charred and ruined, the harbinger of a pinched and emaciated winter to come. I will surely not live to see it. The roads are deserted, the crops untended. The land has gone to seed.

On the flat approaches to Gorey, a magnificent carnival of war is on display around the tents and cooking fires of the French royal army. Two thousand knights have come here to overpower our garrison of twenty. The invading soldiers stand drilled and ready, preparing for battle with haunting songs of unrequited love and bloody victory. They are clad in heavy black helmets and wear rough, battle-scarred breastplates over leather jerkins. They spit, jostle and drink watery ale. Their axes hang from their belts like meat cleavers, and the hair on my neck stiffens.

Beyond them, the flower of French chivalry stands in full military conference. I see their finest Knights shining blindingly in the sun, as their fresh armour reflects the light like polished mirrors. This resplendent council-of-war is doubtless considering its tactical options. They will be debating in the refined, elegant dialect of the Ile-de-France, the rich heart of the kingdom where many of these lords hold vast ancestral estates. This little northern Island is a mere irritation to them, a speck of dirt that would scarcely fit into one of their baronial vineyards. They don virginal white garments, draping robes of lilied snow over their armoured shoulders. High above them, a splendid blue and gold standard flutters languidly, sporting the bright *fleur-de-lys* crest of their royal master.

Their absent King, Charles the Wise, has fought back with verve and aggression to avenge the humiliating treaty of Brétigny some thirteen years before. Time and again, he has repelled the fierce swordsmanship of the Black Prince. He has survived vicious arsenic poisoning and bears the abscesses to prove it, and it is said he feels he has nothing more to lose. Such an enemy will fight like a wild dog. His very name recalls the majesty of the Emperor Charlemagne, and even the Holy Father flutters restlessly under his wing at Avignon. Jersey is merely another way-marker on the journey to fulfil the patriotic dream of his bards. Their dream is to forge the ancient realm of Gaul anew, as a single fat hexagon of land, one realm under one King. And that King is not ours.

Beyond the garish knights, I cast my eye over a village of tents, horses and supply wagons; the usual long tail of retainers, blacksmiths, cooks and whores that cling like parasites on to the entrails of any grand field army. Stables of royal horses, the finest thoroughbreds from the stud farms of Languedoc, snort hard and await their masters. On the slope beyond, siege engineers inspect their monstrous factories of war. This will be no mere peasant-hunt as at Grosnez, but a professional military operation, worthy of the ancients. Immense wooden mangonels stand poised to rain angel fire upon us. Their escalades, great wooden ladders designed to mount our walls, are forged and ready. Meanwhile the sappers are planning their excavations. It will not be long before these skilled and tenacious miners are ready to weevil in to bring our walls down.

Now the ants are beginning to stir. I spy a priest scuttling among the ranks, displaying a handful of dried bones to the soldiers. He scatters a smattering of dust over them. The knights genuflect and cross themselves before the holy relics, imbibing the power and protection of their saints. Then a cheer erupts as the commander's tent opens and the Black Dog himself steps forwards. I am reminded of the words of the prophet Isaiah. Du Guesclin has "no form nor comeliness, no beauty that we should desire him". Yet this Frenchman is no saviour. He has gorged himself too long on the gluttony of war, feasted on the hearts of men, sold his soul and mortgaged the proceeds. They say he is scarred and mutilated, carrying the bitter legacy of half a hundred campaigns. Of course, the men adore their lucky general. It pays to be a winner.

Suddenly there is a lurch, a flurry of cries, a searing call to arms. The leper-house opposite the castle is now aflame; its poor inmates leaping like fiery spirits as they flee the carnage. Men laugh uproariously at the sight. A brace of abandoned boats is blazing down in the harbour below us, spewing wrecked timber into the rising tide. The French army is on the move against us.

As if in a dream, I watch the circus of war commence its first act, a sublimely choreographed display as familiar and ritualistic as holy rites. This hallowed drama would be as familiar to the legions of the Roman Empire, and indeed the ancient Imperial tactical manual of Vegetius remains our lodestone and guide for the art of war. So the infantry roar towards us across Castle Green and they approach the brute outer wall of our bailey. My archers are defiant and, heaving with sweat, they unleash a deadly black shower. Gravity does its inevitable work, and a cloudburst of arrows makes searing, bloody contact. The cries curdle my blood. Hardened French warriors scream like babies and curse like thieves as the missiles savagely impale their innards. Then we launch a hail of heavy, jagged rocks, cascading down in an avalanche from our battlements, fracturing skulls, puncturing lungs and brutally pounding their limbs.

One daring and reckless assault team succeeds in mounting an escalade right against the walls, and a dozen brave Frenchmen start to climb, screeching of the glory of their king. My archers soon douse their enthusiasm with a flaming tub of liquid oil that drenches them from above. The shrieking, scalded victims tumble to the earth like flies. The Frenchmen start to withdraw, in a disciplined tactical formation. Our hearts are pumping fiercely with the exertion and elation of battle. We are drenched with sweat and reeking with fear, and the pungent stench of death smothers us like fog. It is high summer, and the fallen French bodies are already thick with flies.

Only a fool might think we have seen them off. A brace of Du Guesclin's men have been slain here, the nameless and disposable dead piling further honour and renown on the house of the Valois kings. I imagine a dozen more will submit themselves later to the butchery of the field infirmary, and all will receive the last rites despite the best efforts of their physicians to bleed them. But I also know that wise eyes will be watching this apparently futile frontal assault. There is a cold method in his madness.

Du Guesclin will surely now understand our strength, disposition and prospects. I can sense his calculating mind whirring as subtly and powerfully as the intricate astronomical clock of Padua. It is plain to see that the escalades he shipped over from St. Malo are too short to top the walls, and he will doubtless crop the ears of his carpenter for this embarrassing miscalculation. Yet this is of little import. To Du Guesclin's forensic eye, the density and cadence of our arrow battery will speak a story of utter weakness, not formidable defensive strength. He will have easily calculated that we have only a handful of trained English archers to defend the battlements.

On the horizon, we have already spied his royal engineers at work, skulking by the seaward curtain bastion, evaluating its construction under cover of the frontal assault. We know our outer walls are crude, and now the secret of our frailty is exposed. The finest sappers that the King of France can muster will be unleashed on us tonight. And, on the seventh day, Jericho will surely fall.

Hours pass and the hot day slides into a dismal and fetid night. After the frenzy of the charge, our handful of English archers sprawl uneasily on their straw pallets, dog-tired, sharp-breathed, with the wan and bloated pallor of hounded stags. The humid night closes in as the Jersey watchmen tread the outer curtain wall. We are under siege. My master-at-arms coyly scoops a glance through the arrow slits, surveying the scatter of dying campfires, ears catching the murmuring hubbub of this great invading army.

The air is drenched with sweat, soot and horse manure, mingled with the overwhelming stench of the rotting dead lying in the killing fields by the wall. The gods of war are feasting well tonight. Fainter and further away, we all perceive the relentless thud of hammer and chisel, the heavy sacks of dark earth rustled from unseen boreholes and secret tunnels. We are no fools. We know their moles are tunnelling, knee-deep in their own sweat, caked blind with dirt and stone, coming to kill us. And when Jericho fell, all were put to the sword.

The broken walls of Jericho are richly illuminated in my wife Margaret's book of hours. She smiles at me and tucks the breviary under her arm. I am walking with her again in the gentle bowers of Hemyock, the King's commission in my hand, surrounded by a grove of pear trees. Springtime. I know I will be returning to the Islands, and she sheds a tear. I look out over my beloved soft Devon hills, undulating before me like the waves of the sea. It is a clear and magnificent April day, when the skies are still young and gifted with promise, and then I hear the sound of approaching hooves, bearing down, hammering towards me…

I lurch from my mattress, jolted awake by a deafening, unearthly shriek. I shudder for a moment despite myself. Military discipline reasserting itself, I draw my sword, and stagger to the turret. I feel like a jester, miming my parts, silenced by the avalanche around me. The floor roars and shudders around us and I curse like a fool.

The curtain wall is falling. As if in a dream, I watch the vast, grey and cavernous stonework collapse on itself, falling in a massive whirlwind of acrid, choking dust and a hail of great rocks. The thunder is all consuming. At long last, the terrible slide is done, and the screams of the dying are heard again above the din. Fires burn sullenly at the base of the livid breach. Silence ensues, a long, painful and exhausting gap as my broken heart slams into my chest.

I order the retreat. "To the Keep!" My archers diligently comply. Yet a handful of the local men, perhaps deafened by the blast or intoxicated with the deadly mead of courage, choose to fight. They stand and raise their swords, spitting curses into the darkness. They are duly slaughtered like wild hogs.

A hundred armed men surge into the bailey, bristling with pikes and armour, screaming of victory and glory. They seize our supplies, poison our wells and put the survivors to the sword. Du Guesclin is at their head, a pugnacious and rampant toad. The Black Dog is brimming with pouting arrogance, as he runs the hares to ground. He barks orders from his horse like a petty Caesar, strutting with the consummate ease of the master. No coward he. No fool.

When the inevitable demand for terms comes in the morning, I reply as my royal duty bids me: there shall be no surrender. My head would be on the block for anything else. And from the outside, my Keep looms impregnable, secured by vast walls that even the fires of Doomsday could never break. The angel rolled back his scroll, the seas fled, and still Gorey Castle stood invincible.

Appearances deceive. This place will be a mausoleum, our sealed tomb.

He knows, and I know, that my cisterns are running dry.

The Cycle of War

William of Asthorpe agreed terms with Constable du Guesclin within weeks. He agreed to surrender, should a relief force not arrive by Michaelmas. Honour was technically satisfied on all sides and the restless French Constable departed these petty islands for a greater prize. A token siege force remained.

On September 2, 1373, the Admiral of the Fleet relieved Gorey. The three lions of Edward III, the banner newly quartered with lilies to emphasize his French inheritance, flew high once again over the battlements.

Yet the vicious reign of War had not ended. The butcher's bill was still in the counting. The blood price would lengthen as long as there was pride in the hearts of men. As long as rival kings clashed over scraps of rock, like blind men squabbling over a glass eye, Jersey would pay a heavy toll. Tax, toil and tribute flowed away to distant realms. And in due season, the fatal prophecy of Jericho would be fulfilled. The French army would return again to Jersey. This time, treachery would prove stronger than stone. This time, the Castle would fall.

The savage cycle of war raged for generations, the islands mere playthings in the thrall of rival kings. In 1406 the Castilian corsair, Niño, landed with his locust army to sweep Jersey bare. His scavenging soldiers pinned the natives down into their last redoubt, an ancient hill-fortress set deep in the northern parish of Trinity. The harassed men of Jersey simply paid off their foreign tormentors, their humiliation painstakingly counted out in ten thousand gold crowns.

Yet the fortunes of war could turn as swiftly as the rising tide surging in over the broken moonscape of La Rocque. On St Crispin's Day 1415 came the fleeting splendid victory of Agincourt, the high water mark of glorious English myth. As the flower of French chivalry was ruthlessly culled like poppies, the hinges of history seemed to swing shut with fatal decision. Yet final English victory became a quest as pyrrhic and elusive as the Holy Grail, and fate proved itself in the end to be as fiery and mutable as quicksilver.

It all began with the vision of a French peasant girl in her father's garden. Stunned by the miracle of the heavenly lights, her life blown apart in a single Damascene moment, this simple virgin became an apocalyptic warrior. They called her a saviour, a witch, a heretic. She called herself Joan of Arc. Her artless prophecies struck through flesh and bone with the piercing force of a crossbow bolt. She conjured fanaticism and inspired sheer faith, energising the devastated French nation like wild lightning from heaven. The English army was left confused and retreating, crumpled before her power like broken reeds in the autumn winds.

History simply unfurled at her feet.

They burned her at the stake, but her spirit came back stronger. As the scales tipped and the English crown rattled off the French seaboard like a lost wager or a tumbling die, the islands fell into shadow again. England slipped into the living hell of civil war, blood against blood and father against son. The morsels of land in the bay were fair game, ripe for the plucking.

So the Castle at Gorey did fall, and it was treachery that opened the gates. The entrepreneurial French raider, Jean Carbonnel, claimed Jersey as his prize and his army stayed for seven long years. The victorious French confirmed the privileges of the ancient estates – the legal bench, the clergy and the parish officials – and the States of Jersey began to assume its embryonic form. History could have so easily subsumed these francophone islands into the eminent domain of France. The course of history would have been utterly different; with Jersey sending deputies to the Estates-General, clashing in the French wars of religion, drawn inexorably towards the autocratic splendour of the Sun King, the reflected emptiness of the Hall of Mirrors and the petrified, rotting glory of the old regime. That future never happened. The town named after a beheaded saint would be spared the mass slicing of the "National Razor", and the tumbrils would never roll past a desecrated Town Church to feed a hungry guillotine in Market Square. History, it seemed, had other plans.

In 1468, after nineteen weeks of fierce siege, the Seigneur of St Ouen and the Yorkist commander Harliston smashed through the last line of French resistance at Mont Orgueil. The defenders had engaged in desperate, frenetic boat-building to fetch supplies; their final ruse failed. The stream of history changed direction, and the course that led directly to the bloody birth of the French Republic was diverted forever. When the final reckoning from the Hundred Years' War was done, Jersey stayed aloof from a resurgent and unified French kingdom, a little lost fragment of old Normandy drifting in the Gulf of St Malo. The Islands became historical anomalies, curios: worlds apart and out of time. They were mere flotsam in the tide, and who knew where the turbulent currents of history would drag them?

Horizons

Jersey 1468 – 1618 AD

The World Changes

*T*he long and terrible war had ended. But events half a world away had set in motion an avalanche that would change the world, and this tiny Island, forever. They say a single spark can set a great forest aflame, and so it proved.

In May 1453, a blood moon hung high over the doomed Oriental city of Constantinople, a red harbinger of death that dealt panic among its defenders. Four days later, the glowing fire of St Elmo raged high above the besieged walls. The glory of Rome, it was said, was finally departing the city. The Roman Empire, in its final and ossified Byzantine incarnation, was about to fall to the might of the Sultan. And as the Ottoman janissaries surged through the ancient streets, the Imperial Library of Constantinople was thrown open and ransacked. The floodgates had been opened after generations, and the accumulated secrets of the ancient world were literally unlocked and set free. Greek scholars fled west, taking their wisdom with them.

Ideas spread like wildfire. This was no mere joyous rediscovery of ancient truths. Soon a tremendous upward spiral of invention and art and science transformed the city-states of the northern Italian peninsula. The great humanist project of literature and learning flourished across Europe, scattering abroad the closely held and cloistered secrets of the clergy. Eventually, fuelled by the technology of printing and the giddying new wine of the undiluted, unfiltered gospel, men started chafing at clerical power and dogmas. Jersey's medieval parish churches stood intricately frescoed, ornately engraved, richly adorned with saints. Few could have foreseen that within a generation these Jersey altars would be stripped bare, walls stark and whitewashed, the Island's priories ransacked. Religion would soon leap out from the mysterious and ancient cloak of ritual and image and encode itself in the pure, literal power of the Word.

The Fall of Constantinople changed everything. Their trade routes blocked by the new power of the Ottoman Empire, a new generation of adventurers sought new supply lines across the seas, to the west. Merchants desired a direct and lucrative route to the spoils of Cathay. They discovered not China, but terra nova, a new earth, and they fought like dogs over the spoils. Even as bloody confessional wars ravaged Europe, the great powers jostled over the new realms in the west, casting empires like nets over the fresh vistas of the New World. And the first Jersey fishermen slipped across the endless horizon of the western ocean to plunder the Grand Banks of the North Atlantic.

As the sixteenth century neared its close, Spain and England were locked in mortal rivalry, fuelled on both sides by the fire of religious zeal. A great Armada sailed against Queen Elizabeth but was dashed to pieces, as if Providence had spoken its verdict. Skirmishes ranged far and wide across the globe, and the horrors of war propelled a new breed of aggressive English buccaneer to fame.

In the wilderness of North America, these men planted colonies, and one of these pioneers was the fabled Sir Walter Raleigh. He established a settlement on the wild shores of Virginia. This first colony died a mysterious death, swallowed up by the forest, but it captured the imagination of an age. Strange discoveries made their way home from the New World – pipe tobacco, and the humble potato, and Raleigh was the chief evangelist for both. He was often seen wreathed in smoke, like a shabby warlock touting his wares.

What to do with such a restless, dynamic and dangerous man? He boasted a mercurial spirit of bottled lightning, powerful yet destructive, and was best placed at a safe distance. There must surely be somewhere, Queen Elizabeth mused, where his subversive talents could be put to use, where he could not do too much harm. A little kingdom of his own, perhaps. A small Island would suffice. Jersey.

The Governor's Story: Sir Walter Raleigh

Y̶ou do not truly know me, even though my fame runs ahead of me like a whispered curse. Look beyond my swagger, my flamboyance and my braggadocio. My eyes are cold and weary. They have seen strange and terrible things.

I remember the Atlantic campaigns, where the strawberry trees bloom red in the cold November days. I remember the wild surf flooding in and the sea crests frolicking like horses along the endless curve of the bay. My sword was as sharp as the spring gales in those days and a consuming hunger raged in my bones. I was a young buck then, and full of fire. The mockers call me godless now, they love to whisper seditious charges of atheism and apostasy, but then I was gladly in thrall to my Cynthia, my bright goddess of the Moon. I felt her guile luring me in, dragging my men across the bay, my body and strength at the service of Elizabeth the Virgin, the queen of my heaven. So I plundered and feasted for her glory, and I sired unknown children in a barren land. The song of my blood surged and soared with the tides. The mountains brooded over me like jealous gods.

I remember a white flag of parley, fluttering forlornly in the harsh Atlantic sky. I remember the foul storm front, the piercing redness of the berries on the trees, the deep lushness of the green fields and the ageless, barren rocks. I remember the Continental armies filing past in sad surrender. I will speak no more of those iron days. Where the cliffs splintered into the sea, I sold my soul. Under the black and shrieking skies, I carved my name in blood.

The curse haunts me still. I am the sea captain who forded the Orinoco River and gloriously plundered the jungle kingdom of Guyana. I have sent fire ships into Spanish harbours at sunset, singing the King of Spain's beard at Cadiz like Drake before me. I have seized stately galleons overladen with gold and amber, groaning with the sheer weight of ingots and balsam and New World treasure. I have been consort to the Sovereign, lavishly entertained guests at my Durham House mansion, and established colonies of brave men in the new and distant world of Virginia. Yet as I approach my new Island home, and as the Atlantic tides burst harsh upon these bleak beaches and rocky crags, all I feel are the ghosts of my darker, earlier days.

I have said and done too much. Still, I have at last my reward, my sinecure, a final benediction from a fading celestial star, a parting gift from a dying queen. Glory has always been fleeting, that coveted seat on the Privy Council has forever eluded me and my wealth seems a tantalising mirage, seeping away like quicksand. I am dogged by the jealously, the backbiting, the black shadow of scandal that never gives me leave to rest. Only the fear remains.

The curse is deep within me, hounding my dreams, but perhaps this little kingdom will help salve the pain of my original sin. For the Isle of Jersey is now mine to rule, a fit toy and charge for an ageing man who has learned little and forgotten less. I am, for all my sorrows, Sir Walter Raleigh, knight and emissary of the Virgin Queen. I warmly greet you, the Bailiff and Jurats and Constables of this Island. I am your new Governor.

The Jurat's Story: Philippe Romeril

The States of Jersey, 1602

So this, it seems, is greatness. Raleigh sashays in to the States Chamber, immaculately clad in silk and draped in the finest Court fashion. His charisma is beguiling, his eloquence gracious to a fault, the poise and deportment worthy of a great courtier of the realm. He speaks French, the bosom language of our isles, and his beguiling words charm their way into the most obstinate Jersey heart. His carefully coiffured beard, piercing eyes and mantle of celebrity prove an enervating combination. The perpetual wreath of tobacco smoke that clings to him lends him the air of a wise wizard, or perhaps a cheap conjuror. Sometimes it is hard to know the difference.

We men of Jersey feel suddenly ungainly, yoked by the tethers of our manorial inheritance, bound to this island soil but genuflecting to a sea captain who has danced like light across the oceans of the world. Our assiduously cultivated local grievances and grudges, our factions and hatreds, seem baffling and petty to a man schooled in the subtlety and wiles of Gloriana's court. We quarrel over parochial boundaries and offices; he cavorts at the heart of a vast spider's web that spans many kingdoms. The court, he laughingly reminds us, is a king's game, and for the more part played on scaffolds.

Raleigh fizzes with unnatural energy, a coiled spring of ideas and intuitions and plans. He changes the course of history on a whim. So many matters to attend to. Defence, land, education; the work of a Jersey Governor is never done. There is the rigorous administration of the Queen's justice, the bounty of her charity for the poor, the vexing matters of property rights and taxation and local grievance. All require imagination, negotiation and tact, not merely the stroke of a pen to solve. Hence Raleigh's visits are a maelstrom of action, fuelled by the urgency of a man who surely sees the writing on the wall, as the glorious Indian summer of our Virgin Queen limps ever closer to a long and cruel winter. Everyone fears the future, yet few dare voice their fears. Elizabeth's womb is barren, her frailty the subject of constant speculation. She has the heart and stomach of a lion, but these days she has the body of an old, old woman. And when the crown goes north, to the Scots King, this flatterer, this popinjay, this flamboyant courtier will be drowned like a butterfly in the November rain. Raleigh sings so brilliantly because he knows his time is short.

Matters of military importance come first. Our Governor cut his teeth on field campaigns during the French Wars of Religion, and he has seen the internecine hell of civil, confessional war from the inside. Everyone knows the old castle at Gorey is a liability, a redundant anachronism in this age of devastating mobile field cannon and accurate modern artillery that can be aimed at it from the adjacent hill. Its brute hulk is an affront to our pride, a disturbing remnant of our dark medieval ancestors, of all their savagery and superstition.

The fashion is these days for low-slung, star-shaped bastions, enabling carefully orchestrated fields of fire and perpetual surveillance. Location is paramount. So we seized the medieval Priory of St Helier, for who needs that fat relic of clerical greed now the religious orders have been purged? It is now being converted for military purposes. The tidal islet in the bay happens to be an excellent strategic vantage point, with sweeping command of both town and harbour, and the military architect Paul Ivy has proved himself to be a superb organiser of both men and matériel. So under our new Governor, construction has proceeded apace. The upper section, which we call the Mount, is now armed with four cannon. Raleigh dwells, during those short spells when he chooses to grace us with his presence, in the Governor's House. Fort *Isabella Bellissima*, he calls it, in honour of the searing beauty that once illuminated his world. Elizabeth's radiance still lingers on at sunset, ghostly as the white lead of her face powder, a shocking harbinger of an unsullied death mask.

Our Governor, for all his vices, gives credit where credit is due. Our Flemish engineer has done good work, and Raleigh has recently commended him up the line to Robert Cecil himself with these words: "It hath been happy for me if Paul Ivy had remained to finish what he had begun there – which I assure you Your Honour, by the living God, is as praiseworthy a work, both for his judgement, invention and industry in saving charge, as ever any man beheld. And I have not seen a device of that place and pride in any place in Europe". The eulogy is fair. Even we in the truculent States have to agree.

Sir Walter has spared no expense in flattering his patrons, with the Royal Coat of

Arms in all its heraldic opulence exquisitely rendered on the Queen Elizabeth Gate. Rather generously, he has even honoured former governor Sir Anthony Paulet by including his crest as well on the stonework. Considering he brazenly coveted the Governorship from the moment Paulet's illness became public knowledge, it was perhaps the least he could do. Rumour has it that Raleigh intends to carve his own coat of arms over the Iron Gate when he next returns to his domain, and knowing the character of this astonishing peacock, that would really be no surprise.

All this would be enough. But there is more. By some quirk of chivalric allegiance or antiquarian insight, Raleigh has actually blocked the demolition of the outmoded and redundant military installation of Mont Orgueil. Quite justly, he abolished the *Corps de Garde*, the onerous military obligations on the men of Gorey. He tore down their guardhouse. Yet his quixotic decision to maintain this distinctly unfashionable and ugly castle is perplexing, surely an embarrassment to any self-respecting Jerseyman.

On 15 October 1600 I hear that Raleigh wrote to Robert Cecil; "It is a stately fort of great capacity, both as to maintenance and comfort, to all that part of the Island next unto Normandy, which stands in view thereof; so until I hear further Her Majesty's pleasure, I have left at my own charge, some men in it. And, if a small matter may defend it, were a pity to cast it down, having cost Her Majesty's father, brother and sister – without her own charge – 20,000 marks in erecting". So perhaps his apparent lapse in architectural taste is not so inexplicable. It might simply be the cold, mercenary calculations of an old privateer talking after all.

Our Governor's energy is both invigorating and draining. He is a buccaneer of new ideas, dreaming of tobacco plantations in Jersey and trading posts. For centuries our Island has been swathed in fields of fine golden corn and the quality of our wool is legendary. (Why else, indeed, would the phrase 'jersey' be used in common parlance?) Yet Raleigh, like a workman with a hammer who sees every problem as a nail, is forever harping on about the potential of his beloved potato. His fancy is that this tuber from the New World, the talk of London society dinner parties, could one day grow on practically every slope and field in the Island. We nod politely at this fantasy and let the conversation move on.

Some of his less madcap ideas have happily come to fruition. He has this year established a registry of good title – *Le Registre Public* – that will ensure that all hereditary contracts in the Island are centrally recorded. On July 24th, 1602 this scheme was unveiled in the States and we trust it will end the hazards of fire and flood on manorial charters, the pain of costly repossessions and the ever-burgeoning pockets of our Jersey lawyers. Soon he is off to levy import duties, build defences against the Spanish threat; a whirlwind of restless and relentless activity.

And finally another project, another ploy, is unveiled by this swashbuckler who seized treasure-ships and planted Virginia colonies, but as we remember all too well, neglectfully left the settlers languishing there to die. It is now time, he argues vigorously, to found a new College in St Helier, to replace those rotten old public schools of St Mannelier and St Anastase. A few educationalists attempted the same a few years back, but old Rev. William Snape had fled the Island like a fugitive and the fledging college was left rudderless. So who should take over now? The usual backbiting ensued, with Philippe Maret of Trinity turning down the post of schoolmaster as he considers it an affront to his lofty ambitions. Sir Walter is visibly irritated by the endless blockages, excuses and rivalries. He exhorts the eager young teachers, Jean Pallot and Jean Mollet, to persist in their labours and he bestows additional funds to encourage them.

Then he expounds his plans; bold and brash, for the abolition of creaking old St Manelier's and the foundation of a modern Grammar school. Let me be honest. Raleigh intimidates all of us, with his sweeping erudition, his talent for chemistry and astronomy and his roving eye for novelty and fancy. He is rumoured to be an artful poet, as elegantly poised with the pen as he is savage with the sword. So we dither and grumble. Then Raleigh pulls his trump card from the hat: the Seigneur of Trinity himself has agreed to unite St Mannelier with the new College, and will allocate funds for that purpose.

The States conceded defeat in due course and agreed to consider the proposals on his return. These are English ways, English ideas, but we swallowed our Jersey pride and loyally thanked the Governor as he departed for Court. And like a dazzling mirage, he was gone, off to England to pursue his ventures and quarrels and ambitions on a more elevated plane. We breathed a sigh of relief and returned back to our feuds and our farms, to the petty and truculent ways of our fathers.

We could scarcely guess on that day that Sir Walter Raleigh would never return to Jersey. Perhaps his dreams of a new College will lie in the dust for centuries, waiting for another Queen, another age.

The Governor's Story:
Death at Old Palace Yard

The Old Palace Yard, Westminster - 29 October 1618

The curse finally caught up with me on a cold and cheerless spring morning, gripping its claws around my throat as violently and subtly as a thief in the night. Cloistered on her deathbed at Richmond Palace, an old woman, full of tears, finally slipped away into the blackness. The heavens emptied of stars. The bright alluring supernova of the Elizabethan age burned itself out to a shrivelled, blackened husk. My lodestone and love was gone, and the skies wept.

As that stubby bully, James Stuart, leisurely progressed down from Scotland to claim the English throne, the bitter contours of my future became clear. After the funeral, I was stripped of my cherished post as Captain of the Guard. My family home of Durham House was forfeit. Then rivals wormed their stories, suspicions fell like daggers; half-truths were propagated and bred. Dark accusations of old crimes were levied against me. The lies thickened like weeds. They claimed I had openly sought to overthrow the new King. They whispered that I sought to place Lady Arbella Stuart as a mute puppet on the throne of England.

Jersey lay at the epicentre of this maelstrom of accusations. I stood charged with high treason, with inciting a Spanish invasion, seeking to use my little kingdom as a staging post for a new armada. Cobham in his rash confession claimed he would seek five or six hundred crowns in funding for the revolution from the Spanish king, and that "he and Rawleigh agreed to meete in Gersey upon his coming owte of Spayne, and then they would take the advantage of the discontentmentes of the people, and thereupon resolve what was to be done".

So the governorship of my beloved Island was stripped from me, seized from me without trial. The walls of my dank prison cried out with torture and pain, for in this place hopes were broken like traitors on a wheel. So that night, alone in the Tower, as the miasma of London drifted like decay over the Yard, as the dark Thames tidewater flowed by Traitor's Gate, I took matters into my own hands. I slashed myself with a bread knife, begging Death to finally take me, grievously wounding myself so I could die like a soldier. It was to no avail. I lived.

The rest of the charade is of no consequence. It began with the theft of my inheritance, my estate at Sherborne. Then the cruel lure of a release; one bright, glorious last dash for gold and glory that ended in the hell-swamps of Guyana and the pointless death of my beloved son, Wat. The tropics of the Orinoco proved as cruel and unforgiving as the wild shores of Virginia. But I fondly remember the soft little kingdom that I made safe and truly loved. A scrap of my heart will always remain in Jersey.

Now the show must go on. A last, defiant smoke of tobacco and a final tour de force of a farewell speech, playing with the crowd like putty, priming and charging their emotions in a last surge of energy from a dying world. The audience gasps and roars. The applause rings sharp like an axe blade in my ears.

I cast my eyes for a final time over the dark square, fixing the hushed and baying crowd in my eyes. I have refused a blindfold. I am leaving behind the tragedy of this dark and squalid world, and the curtain is falling. I extend my arms like Christ. A pause, a hesitation: "Strike man, strike!"

A man's head rolls softly down into the earth. Far away, the storm tide rips across the Atlantic, tearing in towards the shore, plunging the castle causeway deep beneath the waves. A lone gull shrieks its grief under the hollow stars.

EPISODE 5

A New World

Jersey and Newfoundland 1691

Rich Seas

*S*ir Walter Raleigh died on an executioner's block, but his world was the shape of things to come. An Atlantic future of American colonies, plantations and tobacco was dawning. Like John the Baptist before him, this restless prophet had his head served up on a platter to satisfy a jealous king, but his star did not fade. His little Island would indeed one day become famous for his beloved potato. An American city on the coastline he explored would bear his name. The Victorians enthusiastically adopted him as a fellow pioneer of empire, and he became a picaresque fixture of their school history books.

Encouraged by its buccaneering Governor, Jersey had started to play its own part in the exploration and exploitation of the New World. At the dawn of the sixteenth century, credible reports had spread across Europe of a vast fish bank in the far northern ocean – a place where fish were so abundant they literally filled the horizon, as far as the eye could see. And beyond the banks, there loomed the grey, pummelled shore of a new earth.

Rich seas of untold plenty beckoned, and Jersey quickly rose up to seize its share. Raleigh himself had urged the fisheries to expand, and each summer more and more hungry boats set sail from the little harbour at St Aubin to seek out the fabled New Found Lands. The promise of cod, oil and gold lured men to venture west, and the age of Jersey's Atlantic adventures had dawned.

The Shipmaster's Story: Jean Le Cras, *L'Orange*, The Atlantic Ocean, 1691

'We are as near to Heaven by sea as by land'
Sir Humfrey Gilbert (last words, 1583)

The sickening tremor of a giant Atlantic wave explodes onto our little ship, and sends us reeling and lurching like drunkards across the deck. As we pitch headlong, a black wall of water the size of a house rears up ahead, thundering and bellowing high above us like a wounded beast. The prow takes the full brunt of the impact, but our battle-hardened vessel holds firm. I scream an order from the poop deck and my crew scramble to check the halyards and the jibs. We mutter prayers and oaths. We plough on.

The first fingers of light are staining the eastern horizon and the storm front is now close to its tail end, smothering itself out like the dripping wick of an old candle. It has been a savage night. My Jersey woollen smock is deeply stained with congealed layers of vomit and I am drenched in the bone chilling spray of these northern seas. Below decks, it is far worse; exhausted men are slumped on filthy lice infested pallets; a foul pigsty reeking of sweat and dirt, with space for barely half of us to hunker down at once. Our little world spins one last time like a child's wooden toy and regains an even keel as we finally burst through the growling weather front and stay on our relentless course for the Newlands.

We are still a week away from landfall. Thousands of miles of desolate ocean lie behind us with hundreds still ahead, with unfathomable deeps falling away below and the stars burning above us in a cold heaven. I fancy that we are the petty playthings of an angry God, cast down like flotsam on this turbulent and restless ocean. We are fools for gold, desperate for the full third share of the profits that the grasping St Aubin merchants have promised us. I picture them enjoying a glass of wine back home while we wrench our guts out at sea. In this hellish ocean, in the maw of the beast, the lure of the gleaming *livres tournois* that first propelled my ship on its fatal course seems a cruel joke, a dead man's reward.

We left home half an age ago, in the high days of April when Jersey bursts with colour, when the long and bright evenings nurture the crops and the land is soaring again with life and promise. St Aubin's was a hubbub, bustling with preparation for the expedition, as the boats provisioned themselves for the long voyage ahead. Since Sir Thomas Morgan's fine new pier was completed fifteen summers ago, the port has flourished. Cod merchants' lavish houses are springing up like fresh mushrooms along the harbour shore. So much has changed in the Parish since my youth, but one old tradition remains.

At the start of April, every year since 1611, the St Aubin's fishing fleet has gathered at the ancient church of St Brelade. Here, in the old and holy site nestled in the warm and gentle embrace of the bay, we bid farewell to our native land. This solemn ceremony is the *Communion des Terre-Neuviers*, the final sacrament of the fishermen as we set out into the great beyond. There was no joy on that day, simply calm reflection as we contemplated the fearsome and gruelling voyage ahead. Our women, dressed in their finest Sabbath outfits, but their hands wickedly scarred from knitting and weaving, held back their tears. 'This is my body, which is given for you', the minister intoned. 'This is my blood'. Then we sailed away beyond the sunset, three thousand miles beyond the golden arc of St Ouen's Bay, slipping over the rim of the endless western horizon that we used to survey as children from Les Mielles. We had embarked once again for the newfound lands, for the promise of Avalon.

Those who choose to brave the limits of the known world to become *Terre-Neuviers* become changed men, a world apart from the timid land-clingers who still till the seigneur's fields or graze sheep in the little parishes. A common sailor on my boat can earn twenty pounds in a good cod season; at home he would eke out three pounds and likely squander half of it on liquor. The hazards of drowning, death and the searing icy seas merely spell adventure and opportunity to many a young and limber man. The rewards are sporadic, but can be bountiful. And to those who have much, yet more will be given.

We are all changed by the journey. We have witnessed the green fire of the Northern Lights blaze across the Arctic skies. We have slain whole flocks of Great Auk, the flightless birds whose black patches mask their eyes like wounds, whose bones we know are held sacred by the heathen tribes. We have watched as Basque hunting boats chase the monstrous leviathans of the deep, harpooning blue whales the size of ships to butcher them cold for their blubber and bone. And we have sailed on the fabled seas that the Venetian adventurer John Cabot first told of in 1497, threshing with giant cod so numerous that a single hook might snare a multitude. The word spread fast. As early as 1510 Newland fish were being sold at Rouen, and thenceforth flotillas of French, West Country and Basque merchants set out every spring to plunder the rich ocean.

At last, after agonising weeks at sail, we slip over the shallows of the Grand Banks. The dismal shore of Newfoundland is butting up against the bleak Atlantic, a ghost land appearing as silent and barren to us as the surface of the moon. This is the Avalon Peninsula, a rugged and forbidding landscape with only a scattering of tiny settlements. The very name is redolent of the Arthurian legends, the island of myth and promise, where the lost King rests and will rise again. The land sleeps here under the spell of perpetual winter, but the sea is teeming with life. And we have come here to conjure our own alchemy, to turn stinking fish into pure gold.

Our sailing ship touches shore at Jersey Rock, to the south side of Havre de Grace, or Harbour Grace as the English fishermen are wont to call it. Two summers ago we capped this sea-rock with a giant iron ring for mooring our twenty-ton boats, as we will scarcely have need of these fetid giants until the homeward journey.

Our ship is the very first in Conception Bay, so I assume the title of Admiral of the fishery for the year, and a volley of guns duly marks my elevation. The second boat captain will be appointed vice-admiral, and the third in the harbour will be dubbed rear admiral. Out here, the royal writ runs weak, and so I am now become judge, justice and punisher. For all save capital crimes, my word is now law. Here at Mosquito Cove, I will hold my admiralty court.

After the intense boredom, occasional terror and merciless claustrophobia of the crossing, landfall offers some relief but no joy. The terrain here is dark, dense and foreboding compared to our rich and civilised Island. This is a colder, savage world, darkly overshadowed with the scrappy fog forest. These lands appear silent and empty to man, but we have heard bloodcurdling tales of the Beothuk, those natives clad in ochre whose deadly arrows fly at night.

We dub this alien, aggressive land with names that ache of the beauty of home – Boulis Bay, Petit Port, and St John. Lord Baltimore's Catholic enclave clings on down in Avalon itself. On the southern coast is the French hub of Plaisance, where our native Norman French helps us bid and barter for supplies with the Breton and Malouin seafarers. With equal facility, we supply and trade with the handful of rough Bristol settlers who choose to huddle together in Havre de Grace through the bitter four months of winter.

Beyond the Narrows lies the only town of consequence in Avalon, the rugged port of St John's. It was here that Sir Humfrey Gilbert boldly seized the land for the English Crown on the 5th day of August, 1593. It is said his speech was eloquent and graceful, but he drowned at sea before the summer was out. His were glorious but empty words, for out here in this wilderness there is no king, no army and no priests. When the notorious vagabond Peter Easton held court in Havre de Grace and terrorised the shoreline like his private domain, there were no constables or judges to stop him.

So we Jersey fishermen know better than to settle in this unforgiving land. We are mere summer wanderers, migrating from the western fringes of Europe and skulking back in the autumn with our salted treasure stowed safely below decks.

And perhaps after our Atlantic wares are unloaded at the fish-hungry ports of Catholic Europe, traded for wine and food and converted at last to hard coin, we will return home to Jersey as prosperous men.

The dream seems a long way off, and the long slog of hard work begins in earnest on arrival. Last year's huts have been ravaged by the Beothuk as they plunder our nails and iron. So we fell fresh trees from the forest to construct stages on land, where the fish will be salted and pickled. The flakes, or long thin wooden tables, will be the centre of our summer industry. Storehouses, cooking rooms and huts spring up as the men labour tirelessly to build the seasonal cod station. We dub this place the Jersey Rooms.

The men fish in small *pataches*, or little boats with just three men in each: a master, a boatswain and an unskilled man. The crews work diligently and long on the hand-lines, using the bait to reel the fish in. After an arduous morning at sea, when the fog begins to fall on the bay, the fishing boats dock on the shore and hand their precious hauls over to the headers and splitters. This is the filthy, smelly work: salting the fish and leaving them to dry on the flakes. The land here is sparse and yields a poor crop, but the sea offers a magnificent bounty.

In the long summer evenings, when it seems that a half-light lingers over the bay, the men gather round campfires on this alien shore. They recount tales of sea-wolves and bears, stories heard from the local traders who scour a living from this wild land. And they sing tales of lost loves, half-remembered homes and the sweethearts they once promised they would not leave '*por tot l'or d'Avalon*'. Of course, they lied.

It seems the monotony of salting and splitting fish, on the far side of the known world, can do strange things to a man's mind. The reflected blaze of the endless dark blue ocean and the stark wilderness burns like wildfire inside all of our heads by day and night. On our rest days most of the men drink themselves into a stupor, happily forgoing part of the profit share for the small comfort of a grog allowance. Our loved ones, our inconceivably distant families and kinfolk, flit like shadows in our dreams.

The men even tell a tale, that by jumping over a puncheon or vat of water, they can leap home for the weekend, bounding over the vastness of the boundless and cruel Atlantic. On the Sabbath, I prefer to pull a tattered Bible from my breast pocket and idly ponder the fate of Dives, the rich man sent to hell: "And beside all this, between us and you there is a great gulf fixed: so that they which would pass from hence to you cannot; neither can they pass to us, that would come from thence". The ocean is too wide. And all this time the salt fish piles up in the storehouses, the dead fruit of the sea that will earn us our fortune.

The summer rolls on, and there are fresh rumours of strife. The fishermen of Europe are despoiling these seas and lands like vultures, forever seeking new horizons and new lucre. They plunder Anticosti, where whales come to die, and the Magdalen Islands, where they say an hour's fishing with four hooks can yield two hundred and fifty plump cod. The belligerent Dutch have long been a thorn in our side, and now it seems that England and France are at loggerheads again.

And on a languid September morning, some fur traders bring fearsome news. There are rumours that our old nemesis, the French, have sent a troop of soldiers up from Plaisance to scour the Avalon peninsula, burning warehouses and stocks wherever they can find them, perhaps hoping to march on St John itself. The next morning we load the cod and prepare our ship to set sail. We have no desire to find ourselves in the middle of a war. Fish, oil, and profit: that is our simple Jersey calculus, and it has always served us well.

Our anchors are hauled in and we slip away from Jersey Rock. As we sail out of Conception Bay, I try not to contemplate the sheer abyss of the ocean, the perils that lie ahead. They say that when Sir Humfrey Gilbert, the first pretender to this bitter land, drowned at sea, he was calmly reading Sir Thomas More. I learned my French and Latin grammar well enough at St Mannelier's, and as a ship's master I even know a smattering of English, but I am no scholar. Yet More's words have always burned fiercely inside my head. "He that hathe no grave is covered with the skye: and, the way to heaven out of all places is of like length and distance". Gilbert summed it up aptly with his final dying cry: "We are as near to Heaven by sea as by land".

He was reading *Utopia*, and perhaps we found ours out here in the west, across three thousand miles of hellish ocean. This summer's work has yielded a rich sea-crop. The ship is slow and heavy now, our hold bulging with salted cod, groaning with the weight of our stinking fortune. Relentlessly, restlessly, I calculate my lucrative share of the spoils. The tedium and terror of the voyage are a small price to pay.

Suddenly I am jolted from my musings. Our good ship *L'Orange* bucks and churns fiercely as we smash into the open sea. A pillar of smoke is staining the distant horizon; perhaps a last fishing post is burning, or the restless natives are on the move. We have our haul, and care little now. The silent land and teeming fisheries already seem a receding memory, a waning summer dream. Then the smudge on the horizon diminishes and the last shadow of the New Lands slips away, leaving us in the cold hands of the vast and oblivious ocean.

The Winter Spell

*J*ersey duly prospered on the back of its Atlantic lucre and the hauls of thrashing fish would prove a mainstay of wealth for successive generations. The acclaimed and opulent 'cod houses' of Jersey stand today as the grand legacy of its Newfoundland adventures.

Yet far closer to the granite cliffs of St Ouen, a savage tempest was brewing. The lashing seas and blinding hail of the Atlantic paled in comparison to the ominous storm clouds that would soon be bursting in over the British kingdoms.

The latest news from Westminster sent tongues tattling and whispers scuttling. King Charles had forcibly prorogued Parliament and now he chose to rule alone. For over a decade, the heart of England lay suspended, as if frozen under a winter spell. Parliament lay empty for eleven long years, its great doors barred and bolted, as dust gathered in its silent pews. The King reigned in majestic isolation, graciously dispensing justice as the divinely appointed lex loquens, or 'speaking law'.

He shamelessly plundered his realm for Ship Money taxes, emptied the unwilling coffers of the inland counties and lived off the rich cream of his fat monopolies. Charles behaved as a royal revolutionary, seeking to remodel the ancient constitutions of Church and State from within, in his own gilded image. He introduced shocking innovations to worship. He railed off the altars. Dissidents were ruthlessly punished. One celebrated Puritan troublemaker, William Prynne, had his ears cropped and his cheeks branded with S.L., for 'Seditious Libeller'. He was then packed off to the dank dungeons of Mont Orgueil Castle to repent at leisure for his sins.

Jersey and Guernsey were deeply troubled by this nascent tyranny. If a king could subvert the established liberties of old England with such impunity, what hope for the cherished rights of the vestigial Norman bailiwicks that still clung to her coat tails? Still they nobly sought good relations with all men, sensing that a day was coming soon when brother would betray brother. Yet a single spark was about to ignite the barrel of gunpowder, and then the simmering resentment of a muzzled people would explode.

The spark was a new Prayer Book imposed on Scotland. As rebels surged south across the border and the royal treasury ran dry, the King was forced in desperation to rouse the English Parliament from its slumber. This resurrected body would be no tame and compliant beast. Rampaging mobs now owned the streets of London at night, and the King's ham-fisted attempt to arrest five MPs hurled the entire nation over the precipice. As war broke out, Jersey was bitterly *torn in its loyalties. Philippe de Carteret, the Lieutenant-Governor and Bailiff of Jersey, secured its great castles for the King, but the rest of the Island stood in open revolt. Guernsey soon nailed its ardent colours to the Parliamentary standard. Then Philippe died, and by the time his fiercely Royalist nephew George Carteret landed to secure his homeland, the Island's fratricidal wounds ran fresh and deep.*

In the darkened and cramped confines of his St Helier garret, the shrewd diarist Jean Chevalier kept a secret chronicle of these last and terrible days. His words shine like a flickering candle in the gloom, each painstakingly scrawled word of Jersey French standing as a testament to these seasons of gathering darkness.

His foreboding was justified. In Jersey, the skies were about to fall.

EPISODE 6

The Fugitive King

St Helier, September 1649

The Chronicler's Story: Jean Chevalier

> "He hath stripped me of my glory, and taken the crown from my head"
>
> The Book of Job 19:9

In these last days, the world has been turned upside down. The King is dead and his kingdom lies crushed in the dust. Great Britain has drunk deep of the wine of slaughter, pitting brother against brother, turning father against son. Our country has feasted on its young like a serpent devouring its own tail.

The hallowed order of the centuries – king, lords and bishops – has been utterly ruined in a few short years. England today lies bound in chains, the slave of a military dictator. The bishops have been mocked and defrocked and the ancient cathedrals lie desecrated and whitewashed. King Charles himself was first paraded like a common criminal and then hauled for a mock trial before a den of thieves. This hideous theatre reached its climax on a freezing day last January, when God's anointed king was publicly executed.

Even the heavens shed bitter tears as the head of the kingdom rolled down into the gutter. Now Lord Protector Cromwell governs supreme. The white flame of his Puritan revolution is consuming England, as the fanatical zeal of his self-proclaimed godly reformation spreads like wildfire. Frivolities and doctrinal lapses are ruthlessly punished. With ferocious military discipline and a desolate heart, the New Model Army is busy subduing the nooks and crannies of these isles. This very month, Drogheda is burning. Perhaps we will be next.

These are dark days. The royal oak of England has been burned at the roots. The crown has been cast into the dust. Only our blessed scrap of rock clings on, loyal to the end, under the fierce command of Sir George Carteret. We men of St Helier loudly proclaimed young Charles as King in Market Square as soon as we learned of the tragic events of January.

So when a prince is cast down from heaven, where does he flee? Where can a king without a kingdom seek his sanctuary? Three years ago, long before the foul regicide, our young prince found shelter awhile on a little island, far from the storm of the British wars. He knows this is as good as place as any to hide. So the royal star has again crashed down from the skies to blaze on these sandy shores. The King is coming.

Our Duke made landfall on the seventeenth of September, and Philip de Carteret rode into the sea, right up to the height of his horse, to bow low to His Majesty and offer the loyal homage of his fief. Bonfires erupted, guns saluted and bells pealed in joy from St Ouen's on the western dunes to St Martin-le-Vieux in the sheltered east. The royal yacht had evaded two Parliamentary frigates sent down from staunchly republican Guernsey. They soon tacked away out of the range of our cannon range, but loomed over the horizon like sharks.

Yet how low has greatness fallen, how low. God's anointed Sovereign arrived in Jersey amidst a grotesque carnival of corpulent courtiers, minions-in-waiting and wine-soaked buffoons. They are still clad in the obligatory black of mourning, but most wear it without reverence, as if it is simply this year's court fashion. The King's retinue stands at five hundred; a gaggle of dispossessed cavaliers, hot-tempered drunkards and prancing flunkeys draped in silk. It is perhaps no wonder we lost the war.

Charles lands here uncrowned, a fugitive on the run, a bankrupt with a mere handful of livres in his velvet pockets. He boasts neither land nor money, merely the vestigial sway of a fallen monarch. He reviews our straggling Jersey Militia on the sands, as if it were the grand field army of Great Britain. He grants leave to build manorial dovecots and resolves arcane disputes over the ownership of land. It is a pleasing but frustrating illusion. This man was born to rule great kingdoms from the majesty of Whitehall Palace. Instead he is lord of twelve tiny green parishes, caged in by the encircling and treacherous sea.

St Helier Parish Church, September 23, 1649

Our grieving King has come here this Sunday to pray and the skies are black with thunder. This ancient parish church of St Helier, perched where the sea wall meets the rolling sand dunes of the bay, is eyewitness to the plangent sadness of kings.

Young Charles is a lad of barely nineteen, swarthy and of middling height, crowned with a shock of dark brown hair, inclining to black. And since that bitter January morning when the head of his father, Charles I, was sliced off like bacon, the icy weight of the Crown has fallen upon his head.

He has fled to Jersey for his life, to escape the intrigues and mortal dangers that dog his heels like assassins. It shows in his eyes. Young Charles has the look of a man hunted and hounded. His sacred birthright of England has fallen into shadow, and his regal domain has shrivelled to this scrap of rock some nine miles by five.

The rain beats down hard from the Jersey sky, and most of the townsfolk have stayed away, discouraged by the foul weather. The novelty of the royal presence has it seems worn off a little in these last few months. The congregation falls silent in respect as King Charles solemnly enters the Church clad in striking violet, the ancient royal colour of mourning. The pain and loss seared onto his swarthy face are palpable. His countenance is grave, his face frozen by grief. Like a noble and hunted stag, he has come here to lick his wounds and seek to drink from the river of life.

The young King bears no ornaments or finery, except for a single silver star on the left side of his cloak, where his heart rests. He is a youth born for battle, drilled to avenge the murder of his father. Even his pistol holsters and the end of his garter are draped in the purple cloth that enshrines his grief. His younger brother James, Duke of York, stands by the King's side, wearing black. The learned divine Doctor Byam, a distinguished Oxford scholar, leads the service without undue ceremony, to respect our local traditions. There is no hint of Arminian practice here. The service is conducted in that alien tongue, English, but we loyal Normans graciously accept this imposition. For the light of kings has come to dwell among us and shine in our church, and we stand in awe.

His Majesty and the Duke of York kneel on soft cushions, with the Prayer Book set before them, and a divine turns the pages for their royal comfort. As the Court in Exile solemnly prays, the sober warning of Judges weighs on many a mind: "In those days there was no king in Israel; every man did that which was right in his own eyes". In this generation, the prophecy has been fulfilled.

Outside, the Jersey clouds shatter with thunder and the black skies weep. The autumn rain lashes down, seeping deep into the stonework, drenching the world with its tears. The little parish church of St Helier lies in the eye of the storm, and no man can tell when these days of sorrow will pass.

Days of Exile

*K*ing *Charles was richly welcomed by Jersey, a safe haven in his darkest hour. He stayed here until February, enjoying the lavish hospitality of the doggedly loyal George Carteret, who levied a special tax on the Island for the purpose. Chevalier dutifully chronicled each day of the royal sojourn, and his diaries have become a treasure of the age.*

Legends of the royal visit abound. King Charles drew up a map of his beloved Island in his own fair hand; he raced galleys up and down the bay; he spent a night at a little farmhouse by the shore that was immediately christened Bel Royal in his honour.

Even in exile, Charles wielded his royal touch, his mysterious, Christ-like power to heal. One chilly morning, Carteret ushered eleven scrofulous Jersey folk into the Castle Chapel. The invalids knelt before their sovereign. Charles graciously touched them on the throat to cure them of the King's Evil, and declared the royal blessing: "May God heal you". Then a ribbon with a souvenir coin was hung around their necks to mark their day of deliverance. This tradition dated from time immemorial, but in days past his royal forefathers had furnished the money from the copious bounty of the palace Exchequer. Now even the treasure of princes had grown lean and pinched, so each patient was required to supply his own coin.

The King's hand-written note of farewell to Carteret reveals a flourish of genuine royal gratitude. "Carteret, I will add this to you under my own hand that I can never forget the good services you have done to my father & to me and, if god bless me, you shall find I do remember them to the advantage of you and yours; and for this you have the word of your very loving friend. Charles R."

The King's words ring true from the heart, but on the sly chessboard of British politics, Jersey was a mere bargaining chip. Governor Jermyn, Carteret's master, was ever eager to pawn the Channel Islands to the French to curry favour and guns. Hawking off the King's only sanctuary seemed a small price to pay in exchange for a French army to retake London. Fortunately these miry schemes came to nothing; the French were lukewarm; the deal was never done. Meanwhile Cromwell's armies crushed all resistance in their path. Parliament-men ruled Guernsey, Alderney and Sark. Jersey's time was running out.

Charles bequeathed a parting gift before he slipped away to France like a shadow in the night. This dispossessed King, a man who owned nothing, could only promise a magical realm across the ocean. The teeming shoreline of America, vast and uncharted, still fell notionally under the royal prerogative. So this bankrupt

King bequeathed to Jersey a tiny, distant territory known as Smith's Island.

This was no phantasm. Whereas Raleigh's Virginian ventures had ended in folly and disaster, Englishmen had staked a new claim here in the days of good King James. This island was named after Captain John Smith, who was saved here by the native princess Pocahontas. She later toured London to meet vast and curious crowds and soon passed into the realm of legend. In truth, Smith's Island was a desolate and unforgiving sandbar, but here Carteret would be emperor. He was granted leave to establish his own little kingdom, to "build churches, castles and manors, to appoint seigneurs, to establish such laws as he deem expedient". In a final, touching note, Charles chose a new name for the island. It would be called New Jersey.

It was in truth an empty gift from a bankrupt and renegade king. The net was closing in, and the cosy days of George Carteret's little reign were drawing to a close. Cromwell was coming for him.

The Royalist's Story: Sir George Carteret

Elizabeth Castle, November 1651

The game is up, and the final pieces are about to be swept off the board. My swarthy king's writ now runs over a single, battered rock, and in the mulish heart of this proud and stubborn Jerseyman. We are trapped here like rats on Fort Isabella Bellissima, a castle named after the dead queen of a vanished kingdom. We lie stranded here in the bay like beached whales, caught on the wrong side of history and patiently waiting to be speared. The deadly harpoons were delivered today.

We spy them on the shore – monstrous, bloated cannon forged in the pit of Hell. These cumbersome brute beasts have been shipped down from Portsmouth, and teams of Cromwell's finest soldiers have dragged them into the churchyard, propping up these death-dealers upon the black bones of the dead. I have seen them haul up another great gun to the base of the Town Hill, lurking beneath the flags of the English Republic. The cannon are silent and black, gaping as cold as the mouth of hell.

So this is how it all ends. My head is pounding now, dulled with heavy liquor as thick as St Peter's mud, and my thoughts are churning deep back into the secret realm of memory. I am a small boy playing again at soldiers, mock-fighting my way through the granite cloisters of my rambling childhood home at Mont des Vignes. I am scuttling to school, back to the brutal grind of St Anastase where Latin grammar is birched into me without pity or malice. I am a young man again, sailing to the icy Newlands and frisking the pirate ports of steamy Africa. I remember tumbling into love with Elizabeth, setting up home with her in the heart of London, living in the shadow of the Tower. Then came the bitter years of the Great Rebellion, rousing the Cornish royalists, supplying doomed castles, setting up a privateer's palace in St Malo and forcing my beloved homeland to fear God and honour the King. They broke their faith soon enough.

I have supped with kings and fought with common soldiers. I remain as cussed as the earth I spring from, as dogged and defiant as when I first left this rock. The mirage of the royal visit passed in a dream, and the King soon slipped away to the ungrateful bosom of France. Our fond dream of a New Jersey was strangled at birth. We sent a supply ship to claim and settle that little island he promised in Virginia, but a Parliamentary frigate roped them in. Our ship bore the seed corn of a new world – farming tools and thirty good settlers to husband the land – but Captain Green seized them all for the Commonwealth and hauled them back to Wight for plunder. Those regicide traitors have killed our last hope of a new beginning.

I weep for what they have done to my Island. Colonel Heane and his Parliament-men have desecrated St Helier's church, hacking down the pulpit for firewood and stabling their horses in it. Every shred of holy beauty has been burned. The people have turned aside, as fickle as Peter, and the gawping crowds that hailed the King have slunk away in shame, keeping their heads down. The shrill Parliament men, set free from the prison of Mont Orgueil, are crowing now. The soaring black slopes of Mont de Ville loom over us by day and night, swarming with Roundhead armies. These days, I sleep but I do not dream.

As the end of the world is nigh, Elizabeth and I have just taken Holy Communion in the ancient Abbey Church. The ritual comforts me still, a drop of solace in an ancient and holy place. I peer over the black water of the bay, at the gaggle of houses on the sand dunes, at the tower of Helier's despoiled church and the Market Square. Lights are shining in the block fort of St Aubin, now in Cromwell's grasping hands, and the homes beyond cling like black wool to the slopes of Noirmont in this waning November light.

Then comes the Apocalypse. There is a diabolical roar and a cannon flash from the shoreline, a black dragon arcing down from the sky and coming for us with a screeching, demonic hiss. The sheer energy of the explosion knocks me to the ground, but the gunners have fallen short. A second blast roars in, closer and hotter.

Men scream and flee, and I feel a leap of sickening fear surge through me. These men are said to be using a Gunner's Rule, the most fiendish and advanced scientific marvel of modern artillery. Every successive shot will be more accurate than the last. It is only a matter of time. The sands of time are hurtling down now through the hourglass, every last grain, every last memory...

Then the sea is become fire, and the world is red hell. My ears are mangled with the bloody weight of the noise and I am tossed like a doll to crash hard against the stone. I stagger up to see a pillar of flame spiralling up to heaven from the lower ward. The Abbey Church is raging with hellfire from within, its roof collapsed, its walls shredded like sawdust. This house of God that has stood for six centuries has been felled in a single blow. Old words hammer in my head: "The heavens shall pass away with a great noise, and the elements shall melt with fervent heat, the earth also and the works that are therein shall be burned up".

I collect my raging, terrified thoughts. I am alive. The entire gunpowder store – eight giant barrels stored in the Abbey vaults – must have gone up. The flames are simply wild, uncontrollable, and the sheer ferocity of the fire is scourging every inch of stone and grass. My men are scattered in a moment, panicking like dogs, throwing themselves over the walls in a desperate bid to surrender. The tide is low and I see them scurrying for the shore like a pack of cockroaches. I draw my sword to stop them fleeing, and at last my captains mop up a few of the miscreants who tarried too long. These are pale, sad boys, but my heart is burning with rage. They will draw lots soon, and one of them will hang.

The catastrophe finally burns itself out, leaving charred ground and blackened land. Skeletons crawl in the ruins, half-cremated by the incinerating force of the blast. The holy heart has been ripped out from Saint Helier, and, far worse, the last of our munitions has perished in the conflagration. Beating back tears, I send my wife Elizabeth away on the secret night boat to St Malo, and I am left alone.

The jaws of winter close in. I write a final letter to my King in exile, once again begging leave to surrender the Fort on honourable terms. It travels on my last boat, laden heavy with my treasured possessions, my silver plate and jars of whale oil to barter for food. More fool me. The boat soon burns like a Roman candle. Everything is lost.

We crouch shivering in the bay for a few more days, like starving dogs. Then word is received from abroad, and I am granted leave to negotiate our final capitulation.

Jersey has fallen, and the age of kings is over.

Nova Caesarea

*C*arteret dined politely with the victors, and negotiated a handsome settlement of £1,800 and the preservation of his Jersey estates, a final sweetener to end a very civil war. Then he set sail for France and exile, taking to the sea again in the service of the French navy. Yet within six years, he was cast into oblivion. The duplicitous game of thrones had seen a secret treaty between Republican England and the French king. Whispered accusations led to a moonlight arrest, and Carteret was seized at night. He was thrown into the Bastille, the grim and fearsome Paris fortress from which few men returned alive. Locked in isolation, imprisoned without trial, the loyal Jerseyman faced certain death in a French prison. Across the Channel, the iron grip of Cromwell's rule seemed complete.

Yet the muse of history is a capricious and fickle friend. Royal friends pulled strings; the caged bird flew. Carteret fled for his life. In England too, the wheel of fortune was about to turn again. The Lord Protector suddenly died, and the 'force of angry heaven's flame' fizzled into oblivion. After long decades of turmoil and war, the nation turned back to its roots and cried for the return of its forgotten king. King Charles was restored at last to his rightful throne. The Puritan winter melted away and the nation embraced the libertine and joyous era of the Restoration.

Charles never forgot the loyalty of Sir George Carteret and the tiny Island that had stood by his side until the bitter end. Like the Biblical Joseph, Carteret had sacrificed everything for his dogged faith, but in due time was released from prison and exalted to high office in the land. Carteret and Jersey basked together in the royal favour.

The King bequeathed a massive gilded mace to Jersey, staggering in its dimensions and almost as large as the one he gave the Scottish nation. It is clad in eleven pieces of silver gilt and bears the loving inscription: "Not all doth he deem worthy of such a reward". Charles consecrated the gift to posterity as "a proof of his royal affection towards the Isle of Jersey" that had sheltered him when all other friends had fled.

Carteret's personal reward came soon enough. Charles granted a million square miles of primeval American forest to eight of his loyal followers, and named this vast southern land in honour of his slain father, dubbing it the Carolinas. Like Norman barons, these eight great men would carve up this immense land into feudal territories and rule them like kings. One of these lucky Lord Proprietors was Sir George Carteret.

A second gift would soon follow. Long ago, when all England was in mourning,

Icon of Saint Helier by Karen Blampied (2010)

Sir Walter Raleigh, Governor of Jersey 1600-1603

Sir Walter Ralegh by "H" (1588)
(c) National Portrait Gallery, London

Charles II, Jersey's Fugitive King

King Charles II by David Des Granges,
after Adriaen Hanneman (circa 1648)
© National Portrait Gallery, London

Moses Corbet (1728-1814) with Stockades and a Cannon (painted c.1779)
Philippe Jean (1755-1802)
Courtesy of the Jersey Heritage Collections

Postcard view of Prince's Tower
Published by Geo. Barré, Jersey

The Departure of Her Majesty Queen Victoria, 3 September 1846
Philip John Ouless (1817-1885)
Courtesy of the Jersey Heritage Collections

the young James, Duke of York, had knelt beside his brother in St Helier's Church and prayed for a miracle. Now his plea was granted, and he achieved immortality. His armies seized a troublesome Dutch trading colony and the fledgling outpost was renamed in his honour. The name had a certain ring to it: New York.

James too remembered his friends who had stood by him in the hour of trial. In June 1664, he bequeathed a vast tract of his newly conquered empire to two old soldiers who had fought for him: Lord Berkeley and Sir George Carteret. This gift was to be the final fruition of the King's promise that had been dashed so long ago. Instead of a scrappy Virginian sand island, James now granted Carteret some prime real estate: two hundred and fifty miles of fertile Atlantic seaboard stretching south from Manhattan Island.

And so it was that in 1665, George's young cousin, Philippe de Carteret, Seigneur of La Hougue in Jersey, made landfall with thirty bold colonists near the mouth of the Hudson River. On these wild shores, he constructed a few simple log cabins and named them Elizabeth town, in honour of Sir George Carteret's lady wife. From these modest roots, a great tree would flourish.

Long ago, a fugitive king had grieved and prayed in his darkest hour, seeking sanctuary in the ancient cloisters of St Helier's church. He wept, for all seemed irrevocably lost, but his tears sowed the seeds of a new world. The Concession and Agreement of 1664 was duly sealed, and the great Province of Nova Caesarea was established at last. New Jersey was born.

Heat and Fury

*S*o the Restoration saw Jersey's fortunes wax fair, and the Island soon grew fat on the rich plunder of its Newfoundland fisheries. Yet beneath the glorious and happy façade, the first cracks were starting to show.*

Jersey entered the eighteenth century in an unusually truculent and brackish mood. The people still groaned under the painstaking yoke of seigneurial privilege, pinioned just like their French cousins by the archaic straitjacket of the ancien régime. *Feuds festered over church pews, tithes and impenetrable petty grievances. The exclusive aristocratic rights to maintain a rabbit warren (*garenne*) and a dove-house (*colombier*) inspired vitriolic ire in popular pamphlets. Even the operation of the Duke's law ground to a halt as ancient, decrepit Jurats clung like grim death* to high office long after their wits had fled. An imposing new royal prison was built in 1688 at Charing Cross, and all traffic from the west had to pass in a tunnel under its shadow. This was hardly the Bastille, but the fearsome stone gateway hung like a noose over Helier's little town.

The slimy pitch oil of resentment spread, waiting for a single spark. One day the humble silver liard, the prized petty coin of the French peasantry, was unthinkingly debased by a third. Immediately, the repressed rage of the mob exploded. Rioters brandishing pitchforks and cudgels marched from the countryside and stormed into St Helier. The Dean fled into a tavern, swiped himself a cap and greatcoat and fled in disguise to Elizabeth Castle. In the face of this armed resistance, the pernicious revaluation of the coinage was quietly abandoned. The farmers sullenly returned to their fields. This cycle of repression, sulky concession and simmering rage would prove the shape of things to come.

They say that every nation on earth is only three square meals away from revolution. As bread prices soared in Jersey in the 1760s, a wealthy coterie was rumoured to make hay from increased 'rentes' from farmers, which adjusted upwards along with the wheat price. So who were the guilty men, gloating in their wealth as peasant families went hungry? Slippery street agitators cared little for evidence. They wasted no time in denouncing Charles Lemprière, the autocratic and tone-deaf Lieutenant-Bailiff, as crown prince of the profiteers.

Once again, the common people of Jersey marched on their masters, smashing their way into the Court House and demanding a cut in the corn price and the abolition of lordly dues. Under the gentle encouragement of the cudgel, concessions were granted.

As the invigorating spirit of liberty began to stir on the French mainland, Jersey found its radical champion: a gifted orator named Charles Dumaresq. Dismissed as 'maggots' by his opponents, his party proudly adopted the insult as their badge of honour. And so the heat and fury of the riots ossified into two diametrically opposed blocs: the reformist 'Magots' and Charles Lemprière's eponymous band of reactionary 'Charlots'. The Island soon turned ferociously partisan and calcified in its hatreds, bewitched by its own internal squabbles. While Jersey obsessed over its factions, revelling in its bitter feuds, covetous eyes were watching the Island from afar. They saw a house divided, and saw that it could not stand. It would fall like a stray feather in the first storm of winter.

Jersey would prove easy meat.

The Night Invasion

Jersey 1781

Midnight

But of the times and seasons, brethren, ye have no need
that I write you. For yourselves know perfectly that the
day of the Lord so cometh as a thief in the night.

(1 Thessalonians 5:1)

St Helier, Jersey
6 January 1781

*M*idnight has come and St Helier lies dumbstruck under the heart-stopping
spell of a freezing January night. The foul breath of the Jersey winter congeals
on the lintels of a hundred homes, its raw bite insinuating itself deep into the wood,
the harbinger of a cold and bitter morning. The embers of their dying fires throw a
smoky orange pall over the deserted streets where the good townsfolk of St Helier
simper fitfully in their flea-ridden beds. The skies high above them blaze fiercely
with the icy blue stars of winter.

This is truly a night for huddling and nestling, in the leaden streets of St Helier
eclipsed by the looming black shadow of the Town Hill, where even the grazing
sheep cling together for warmth. A gaggle of debtors and other piteous miscreants
howl from deep within the dank prison at Charing Cross, but no-one heeds their
cries. On the very edge of Town, Lieutenant-Governor Moses Corbet is ensconced
snugly in his lavish bedchamber in the Manoir de la Motte. The King's popinjay
turns and snores fitfully, secure in the smug little kingdom of his dreams. In the
early hours, a red moon rises unseen over the open fields to the east and only the

seigneurial doves gently murmur across the dirt track of La Colomberie. Irritated at this intrusion, the town sentry snorts, retches out the entrails of last night's gin and rolls over again with a single muffled curse.

The earth in the frozen fields all around La Motte Street is hard and unyielding and the beaches that lie beyond have been churned and roiled by weeks of turbulent tides. Beyond the huddled boatyards of Havre des Pas, past the dark sweep of St Clement's storm-lashed and savagely eroded coastline, rises a spine of jagged, stark black sea-rocks that could pierce even the moon to shreds.

In this fearsome moonscape, shoals and sands rise and fall like fleeting visions, and twenty foot of rising black water can drown a man faster than he can run. These are ethereal, treacherous lands, a netherworld where the kingdoms of sea and land twist and merge together. Solid anchoring places soon become drowned rocks; gentle beaches lure a sailor like false promises, only to rip his boat to splinters. Only a fool would land here, a reckless madman, a star-crossed buccaneer so drunk on delusion that he cared nothing for the cost. A gambler.

Baron de Rullecourt would be honoured by the compliment.

The Invader's Story: Baron de Rullecourt

There is no heart so honest and loyal that it cannot be bought. A fat-fingered fee and the promise of revenge quickly secured the talents of a treacherous Jerseyman, Pierre Journeaux. Rumour says he killed a man with his bare fists and then fled his parish as a wanted criminal, spat out from the very Island that had spawned him. One man's loss is another's gain, and this traitor's sure knowledge of its secret channels and Stygian tides has led us safe to this hidden landing place. So in the coldest watch of the night, the hour when men are groggy with sleep and conjure phantoms in their dreams, we made landfall on the Banc de Violet. This accursed reef lies about a half a league offshore and is fringed with rocks as sharp as broken glass. My Major d'Herville's sloop was caught on a vicious current and so his barque *l'Oiseau* drifted too far away; but my own ship made safe landfall.

Our black boats moored in the secret watches of the night, and we disembarked like wraiths to drift across this strange lunar terrain. No lights, no fires and no cries: we attack with stealth to close in on Jersey like a hangman's noose. Low and slow we crawl together, over the slimy sea-rocks, plunging through half-drained tidal channels, Neptune's army advancing fast over the frigid bay.

The heart-shock of the water burns me like ice. I am sodden but ecstatic, my spirit surging in a cry of wild joy, and the thrill of the hunt courses through my veins. It is the foulest night, the darkest abyss, the sharpest rock; and we are the masters of it all. The frit and hidebound English will be astounded by our brilliance.

So why have I taken such risks, gambled so hard? It is in my blood, and has since become my bone and meat and marrow. This Legion of Luxembourg is a pack of proud irregulars, a cohort of swindlers, plunderers and rogues. We relish loot and booty and would cheerfully put Europe to the sword for the highest bidder. Our reputation precedes us, and that is why men flee. I am a self-dubbed Baron, a soldier of fortune from Flanders, but I care for no flag or nation. I would sell my allegiance for a sack of gold. I spit on the gentleman's code of combat that binds the hands of more civilised regiments. My men are truly pitiless; last month they even robbed their sick comrades of their winter clothes. So the fat farmers of this truculent Island can expect scant quarter. We carry no fifes or colours; we bear none of the recognised insignia of war. My men will simply gorge themselves on the fat of the land. They will eat what they kill.

As we clamber up the beach at Platte Rocque, we spy a British guardhouse with four cannon. We approach cautiously, ready to unleash hellfire from our muskets, but the shot is not needed. The embers on the grate are stone dead and the watchtower lies abandoned, as empty as the broken bottles of grog on its table. I care little for religion, but a fragment of a half-remembered parable drifts into my head. *If the master of the house had known in what watch the thief would come, he would have kept watch, and would not have suffered his house to be broken up...*

The blind fools have not seen it coming. I smirk as we check our supplies of rope, to ensure we can bind a sufficient number of hostages. Then we night soldiers turn and advance west, tracing stealthily up the little veins of the country lanes until they become arteries, closing in on our sleeping prey. They will slumber just a little longer.

Instinctively, I reach up to my breast and fondle the scarlet sash that I keep concealed here, close to my blackened heart. This is the coveted Order of St Louis, my promised prize, and I have taken the trouble of ordering the ribbon in advance.

Jersey is already in my pocket.

Gunfire in Market Square

*D*aybreak bursts in on St Helier like a volley of gunshots through a window. The army of wraiths swoops like a wake of vultures on its first victims. The Legion of Luxembourg is rampaging brazenly down La Colomberie, crashing and howling like a pack of feral dogs on the warpath.

Poor old Pierre Arrivé, hearing a commotion, opens his front door to lambast the noisy youths and is slaughtered on the spot. Other civilians are beaten and bound. The French mercenaries are breaking into houses now, seizing hostages and raising hell. The town's librarian is bound and gagged, and they drag the artillery commander away in his nightgown and slippers. The Baron's men herd the humiliated Town militia away like dumb cattle. The coup is nearly complete.

At last the final catastrophe breaks upon the indolent, slumbering Lieutenant-Governor himself. Half-dressed, the shell-shocked Major Moses Corbet is roused by the cries of his frantic, dishevelled captain. Minutes later, the French tidal wave smashes with full force into the pomp and glory of the Manoir of La Motte. The hapless Corbet is dragged down from his bedroom like a puppet, and the articles of capitulation are dangled in front of his twitching nose. It will be so easy, so painless, they promise. Anyone would understand, and we will treat you well. At first Corbet demurs, resists and slithers, as if he could bluster for time, but the man with the gun makes the rules. The choice is stark: unconditional surrender, or the first summary executions will start in thirty minutes. De Rullecourt's eyes seethe with venom; he is nothing if not a man of his word.

So fat old Moses washes his hands with unseemly haste, absolving his tortured conscience with the limp excuse of duress, hiding like a child behind the legalistic niceties he learned so well in his salad days as a London lawyer. It is so much better after all to bend with the wind, rather than break. He looks outside over his little houses, the Island streets, now just another provincial French port.

Jersey's capitulation slips from his pen as the winter sun rises. The victorious Baron struts bombastically through town to survey his new domain. He sends out invitations for dinner, and in his magnanimity orders a fattened goose to celebrate. The prodigal Island has come home.

An old roué and ingrate like the Baron should have known that fortune can be a capricious and selfish lover. The story unfolds like clockwork: first struts in hubris, closely followed by its blood brother, nemesis. So the hidden playwrights of history summon forth their wild card. He is by all accounts a bold and capable lad, a young officer of twenty-four. His hitherto unknown name is about to blaze *briefly and fiercely in the heavens, and on these little hinges a great door will turn. Major Francis Peirson marches to seize fate directly by the scruff of the neck, and make it release its prey.*

Peer behind the florid Victorian hagiography and the refined tableau of bloodless sacrifice. The truth of Peirson's fatal charge is raw, pungent and disorientating. For fifteen minutes the angel of death sets up camp in the Market Square, under the blind golden eyes of King George II. The air throngs with cries in English and French, and with the screams of agony that transcend all language. Peirson suddenly breaks through at the head of the brave redcoats of the 95th Regiment, down Avenue du Marché into the Square. A musket ball smashes open his heart. He is dead, and a fearsome and reckless surge of rage engulfs his men. Then the air splinters with gunfire and hearts surge with adrenaline. Blood-red infantry are suddenly flooding down from Rue de Derrière, fired with the hope of glory and fighting with the boundless fury of men who will die to avenge their fallen leader.

Now the Highlanders too are closing in from Vine Street. These are men pressed hard into the King's shilling, their mouths blackened and stained with the taint of musket powder. Their drill is as natural as breathing: rip the cartridge with your teeth, pour in the powder, ram down the lead shot, and aim with lethal precision. Repeat. Kill. Repeat. Men retch at the acrid, choking smell of the guns, the brutal impact of musket balls smashing flesh and bone, earth and stone, the cloying stench of the mounting butcher's bill. The French gunners unleash the town cannon but their shot falls far too high; seared with fear and drenched in terror, they abandon them and flee. Momentum has turned and the French line collapses.

Now the final act in the tragedy begins. Baron de Rullecourt emerges out of the shadow of the old Courthouse now, still draped in the coveted blood-red sash of St Louis. He struts and parades on the steps, shouting unheard words into the mire, dragging the hapless Corbet as a human shield. He is brazenly baiting the muskets and daring them to fire on them both. The desperate gambler is playing his final card. It tumbles stone dead on to the cold flagstones before the foot of a golden king.

The French prisoners, disconsolate, disarmed and dredged up like the flotsam from the neap tide, trudge in to the nearby Town Church. They are herded between the holy walls like lost sheep, their white and blue uniforms singed by battle, cursing the twist of fate that has left them abandoned here. They sing sad laments from distant and warmer lands, dreading the English prison ships, the fearsome hulks, which surely await them. Lieutenant-Governor Corbet guiltily resumes command, even though he too suspects that trial and disgrace are lurking around the corner, waiting for him like thieves.

So in the end there were only funerals: full military honours for the tragic, doomed Baron, laid to rest for eternity outside the Town Church's old western door. Meanwhile Peirson, the brave young man who saved Jersey, lies in honour beneath the pulpit.

The old order will soon change, as history lurches forward again. The kingdom of France itself will collapse within a dozen years, razed by the earthquake of revolution that came, to coin a phrase, like a thief in the night. Yet the ancient parish church of St Helier will remain, with its buried hero and villain entombed here, duelling for eternity. These walls remember, but they will never speak of what they have seen. So the violent heat and pain of an ancient battle is frozen in time here as a marble memorial, or the image on a thousand bank notes, a winter's tale.

The Major's Story: The Court-Martial

Major Moses Corbet awaiting Court Martial
Horse Guards, Whitehall - May 1st 1781

I am falling from my bed and straight down into hell. The nightmare begins in a cloistered courtroom. The panel of illustrious field officers, immaculate in their regalia, peer at me icily across the dry wall of the dock. Behind their punctilious formality and stony silence, I notice an emotion lurking in their eyes, far more corrosive than the bright fury of anger, or the simple clarity of hatred. Its stench hangs unspoken around us, subtle and humiliating, slithering deep inside the whispered asides and furtive glances of these my fellow officers. It is the odour of sheer, pitiless contempt.

I am on trial today in the bowels of Horse Guards, an edifice bleached as white as bone, a modern monstrosity in the Italian style of Palladio. I am cowering here before the Great White Throne of British justice, charged with acting contrary to my duty, to shamefully abandoning my post and delivering my Island over to the invader. My guilt is already made manifest in a score of London rag-sheets and ten thousand coffee house diatribes. I am the traitor who surrendered Jersey without a fight, and the rest is mere detail.

A chink of light breaks into the heavy wooden tomb of the courtroom, and motes of dust turn and swirl around me, like fragments of memory, each one as lost and vapid as my own life. The witnesses have shuffled in here one by one, a lurid carnival of peasants doing their best to flatter themselves and drag me down. The goldsmith and the brandy-seller, the common soldier and the ambitious captain, have together unburdened their twisted tangle of memories before the court. Dragged far off their native Island, these St Helier folk thrash like fish out of water, clumsy and artless before the legal pincers of Whitehall. I see it in the way they move, like slow boats struggling to navigate the maelstrom of London. Still, their plodding testimony, be it conjured under oath and the mortal fear of perjury, is slowly conspiring to drown me.

Like a tidal wave the events of that winter night come flooding back; the night terror of the invading army, that first fall from my bed, my nightcap cast aside and my piss pot kicked over. I rose like a man, cutlass in hand to defend my Island, but was soon hauled and bound, dragged at gunpoint to face the brutish and violent threats of a French gentleman thug. You were not standing there in the Manoir de La Motte, with the instrument of surrender dangling like a sweet apple before you. And if I did not take and eat, I faced the bitter threat of atrocities; the spectre of my town set on fire and put to the sword.

The scene is cut deep into my memory. De Rullecourt thrust his watch down on the table, and he gave me thirty minutes before the first executions began. His army, you must remember, was no regular French formation, but a band of brutes and mercenaries far beyond the letter of the law. And I, a proud Jerseyman, had been abandoned by my commanders, left to face this terror while they swanned off for the winter. I have been branded the scapegoat for their folly.

I resisted, procrastinated, demurred, but it was useless. Lieutenant Ganne exploded with frenetic rage, his thick arms desperate to throttle me. Then de Rullecourt's right-hand man brandished his sabre and threatened to slaughter every man in St Helier. These were bloodthirsty fighters, and they were ready to do it. So I signed the surrender of Jersey to save my people, nothing more and nothing less. If I condemned myself in so doing, it was a small price to pay.

The court's clerk, his spine curved into a perfect hoop, scratches and scribbles my crimes impassively in birdlike shorthand on thick reams of parchment. His dull eyes are barely visible behind his glass-bottle spectacles, the silent scribe of a tragic litany of debts, murders and high traitors. He is dead to the world.

The courtroom rattles on now like a stagecoach at full gallop, eager to press onto its final judgement. The wheels of justice are churning fast through the mud and sand of the coast road, the invasion road, where sparks fly like fireflies off the iron wheels at full speed. The tide is surging in hard around me now, choking me, bringing the French boats in, and dispatching the legions to march and surround and strangle St Helier. I try to stammer out my pitiful excuses for the surrender, but my words mangle into sludge in the dry desert of my mouth. My tongue hangs as heavy as a spiked lead cannon, and I am struck dumb.

Judge-Advocate Sir Charles Gould, the King's favourite, looms over me sly and lean, his pallor as grey as a waxwork. Only his eyes are savagely alive, darting as black as a ferret's, dissecting me with relish like a prize butterfly. As the Honourable Member for Breconshire, squatting unopposed in his own rotten borough, he dares to call my command of a proud Island to account. Trussed up absurdly upon his judgement seat, as powdered and bewigged as a theatre dame, he turns to deliver his verdict.

His thin, aquiline nose quivers a little as he smells some fresh meat, and then he begins to laboriously opine. His chin twitches, barely perceptibly, but a notary, understanding the hidden signal, hands him a velvet cushion. The courtroom gasps. In the centre of the cushion lies a square, black cap, that age-old harbinger of death. I am struck dumb. The motes of dust frolic around me, dancing their last rites in the waning light.

Suddenly Judge Gould rises as high as a mountain above me, and the cap levitates up onto the lofty pinnacle of his wig. Then it thrashes into life, spitting out feathers and blood, a hissing black Corbière crow. I am out on that barren headland now, where the storm fronts crash in like banshees from the Atlantic, wailing over rocks that will surely lacerate and splinter my skull.

Groggy in my nightmare, I rave at the walls of my prison cell, screeching like a tormented inmate in Bedlam. The guards do not stir, for they are no doubt as drunk as my own sentries were on that fateful night. Then I slither back into my thrashing dreams again.

Night terrors continue to lurch at me like drunken convicts, until I am quivering like a fish, lying stinking in sweat-soaked terror. Now the dreamscape twists and turns, into the searing white light of a Palladian palace and the shadow of the noose on the raked yellow sand of the execution yard. I end my dreams as a delicate and bejewelled bird, hammering up against the walls of a gilded white cage, waiting for my wings to be torn.

Eventually the fluttering dies, and the pulsing of my blood slows. Then the sun finally rises over Horse Guards, and as the night horrors recede, the dull ache of reality returns. My court martial will indeed begin today. I wake to the sound of distant footsteps echoing down the white stone corridors, ringing the alarum like the hooves of an approaching army.

The Fatal Dream

The Arctic Circle 1773 to London 1816

The Age of Tumult

*T*he wheels of justice turned, and they yielded an elegant and quintessentially British verdict. The gallows or transportation would after all be a most unsuitable fate for a well-meaning albeit manifestly incompetent commanding officer. Besides, it would be most awkward if the blatant absenteeism of his superiors was to be dragged before the attention of the Court. A noble self-effacing plea for clemency and a dignified silence on more delicate matters would offer the best defence.

Corbet duly coughed up his Lieutenant-Governorship and was shunted off into the silent ostracism of obscurity. His vanishing act was sweetened by a surprisingly generous pension of £250 per annum. The man who lost Jersey for a day died in his nineties, in the bosom of his plump and well-feathered bed.

The military authorities took the near-fatal disaster of 1781 with the utmost seriousness. The Town Hill had proved its worth as a vantage point for the 78th Regiment during the chaotic events of the battle. It was soon transformed into an impregnable, soaring hilltop fortress. Thick granite flanks, eighteen feet high, loomed over the Island and offered clear fields of fire in all directions. The high grassy meadows where sheep once grazed were subsumed into the brute constellation of royal power. The new installation was named Fort Regent, in honour of the as yet uncrowned Prince George.

It was an age of tumult. France fell victim to shocking regicide and revolution, and remained a turbulent and unrelenting threat on Jersey's horizon. Europe reeled for decades as wars begat wars, and Revolutionary fire blazed without mercy across *the continent. Exiles poured in to Jersey and legions of spies flourished, seeking this Island perched on the edge of the abyss. One Jerseyman's story lies at the heart of this seething, eventful age, and his story is one of the most astonishing and tragic of his time. One day they would call him a serene Prince, but in the beginning he just was a Jersey country lad, serving his King in the Royal Navy. He had volunteered to head north on a madcap expedition, travelling deep into a region of perpetual ice. His name was Philippe.*

The Explorer's Story: Philippe Dauvergne

Arctic Circle
HMS Racehorse
Polar expedition, north of Spitsbergen
September 1773

Let me tell you a story about ice. It begins up here in the brilliant circle of the Arctic, the white blindness that corrodes our retinas like witch-fire. As we approach the Magnetic North, all of our fancy veneers have been stripped away, layer by layer, until we are all naked before the blinding snow. We gaze at terrain that no mortal man has traversed until this hour. Deference and rank, learning and wit, wealth and charm are all spent commodities out here, as useless and discarded as a child's toys. They fall into oblivion before the perpetual curse of the cold, cruel sea. The hypnotic, luminous blue of the ice continent draws us ever closer. My heart leaps with joy unbounded at its savage freedom. I never dreamed I would glimpse such mysteries before my nineteenth birthday.

You do not know me yet. I am Philippe Dauvergne, a Jerseyman born and bred, and the desolation of this harsh land has ignited my proud spirit. Some call me a human sponge, and my academic prowess at St Mannelier's Grammar School proved them true. Men often say I have a winning face and courtly ways, and I soon caught the eye of my benefactor Lord Howe, an illustrious friend of my father. He secured me a comfortable berth aboard the Royal Yacht so I might enjoy the first stage of my naval training at ease. My wily uncle James boasts many contacts. He was once custodian of the famous double-headed key to Green Park and Hyde Park, and there he taught King George himself to ride. Perhaps something of the royal touch has rubbed off on me, for my own expectations are accordingly great. My ambitions are forged like a gloriously rifled key, and with luck and effort they will soon contrive to unlock a magical combination of wealth and glory. One day the gates will open for me.

They say that any fortunate hero must first seek adventure, and throw the dice while youth still gives him a dose of reckless courage. My first opportunity soon presented itself with this madcap polar expedition. HMS *Carcass* and HMS *Racehorse* were fired up like cannon shot into the dark and terrible reaches of the far North. Our orders are clear: to reach closer to the Pole than any man before, to seek the fabled North-East Passage. The dream, as usual, is avarice. England is seeking a lucrative proprietary route to China and the East, skirting along the vast northern coasts of Siberia. So we have been hurled up North into this dizzy orbit, far beyond the bulbous golden domes of Archangel and the White Sea, where the ships of the Russian Empress prowl. There are no rival navies here on the edge of the world. Our only guide is Ursa Minor, the Pole Star. The She-Bear herself will carve out our fortune and secure our safe passage through these bitter glacial floes.

The elusive sea-route hangs over us like a chimera in the mist, a tantalising delusion that lures us ever deeper into its wicked spell. Yet every single foray towards the vast ice shelf draws a blank. We are forever repulsed, drenched in torrential spray, land-locked by the fog vapours that hang as murky and cloying as tar. I test my scientific instruments, draw meticulous diagrams, study rare birds, and prise open the natural secrets of this strange new clime. Yet we are no closer to our fabled transit. The labyrinth of ice remains sealed.

I have observed one thing. Life here is primal. It begins in the guano-stained Bedlam of the bird mating colonies, with eggs improbably balanced on the rocks, defying the inevitable fall, the savage law of gravity. It ends in the fangs of a white bear, or drowned in the delirious succour of the numbing ice water. We pass caverns as black as trolls' dens, shoals of stones worn smooth and round by the endless churn of the ice-flow. Seals surface and descend like mermaids, frolicking until a single bear-swipe ends their dance.

We came out here in the dappled height of summer, but the nights still freeze us to the bone. Back in Deptford, they proudly issued us with richly feathered 'fearnought' jackets. These have proved a poor fig leaf for our shivering, delirious bones. Even otter pelts turn to icicles here. At least we travel in the weird glow of the eternal twilight. Whale-men say that December brings perpetual night here, as remorseless and black as a dungeon. Yet Galileo observed that on a winter's night the skies will rage with celestial fire, the aurora borealis, blazing as green as a Jersey valley after the spring rains.

Spitzbergen itself offered nothing but despair. The land here is forged from sheer cliffs, far higher than l'Etacq, fouled by puffin and slimed by great auks. Mountains smothered in perpetual ice glower down at the summer tundra, infested by flies, enjoying their brief frenzy in the sun. They will all be dead by September.

This land once offered a fair haven to the world of men. We landed at Smeerentown, the legendary trading port of the Arctic. Hopes were high, and we came here to barter for supplies, to replenish our denuded victuals. This was the fabled burgh of doughty merchants, diligently coining a fortune on the edge of this white abyss. They say these shrewd and pious traders threw up a little Amsterdam for a season, right here on this icy precipice. The legends were lies, for we found the land gone to seed. Black ruins stand stark like whale bones against the summer sky. High above, the stars melt like candles in an empty heaven, above the permanent eerie glow of the horizon. The blubber pots are grown empty. The fireplaces are frozen. Even the church is a derelict husk. Hope has fled this place.

So we pushed on further and deeper, up into the North, chasing our elusive prize. At first, we were drunk with the beauty of the frozen sculptures around us. The pure blue pack ice, so mesmerising and seductive, blossomed around us like the fallen clouds of heaven. We downed drams of brandy and joyously toasted the King. Our loyal cheers echoed through the measureless chambers of ice. Our delirium soon made us reckless. In the fog, an immense berg loomed at us, a vertical wall of ice, vastly higher than the sheer cliff at Le Pinacle, where the old Roman *fanum* clings on above the scree. Our ship's wheel was splintering under the weight of desperate arms, as we leered and lurched with agonising slowness to slip out of its shadow. We outwitted Death's blank face by a gnat's breadth.

Every scouting expedition failed. Every boat came back with nothing but frostbite and a brace of fish. The doors to the promised garden remained locked, and we had no double-headed key. Our mood soon soured, and tempers flared. Men duelled on the ice, raging and quarrelling over petty honours or perceived slanders. Then one summer night, we awoke to a prison cell.

Our great ships were suddenly encased in ice, the seas as solid as rock, crushing our hulls, as constricting as a snake's jaw. This coup showed no mercy. Our ice-breakers were broken by the ice. Absolute cold was slowly pulverising the wood, infiltrating the English oak, stretching and snapping the strengthened hull from within. Death circled, patiently waiting for our last supplies to run dry.

So we boldly broke out like madmen, dragging our heavy longboats across the ice. We worked like pigs. Our backs ached and our sweat froze solid beneath our inadequate fearnoughts. Painstakingly, we staggered further all day and covered a deceptively weary mile. Men broke down and wept like girls in the driven snow.

Eventually, Captain Phipps ordered a rest, so that we might eat. His Lordship set out his silver service, seeking to dine like a prince on the edge of a precipice. His flunkey set the table and presented the dinner, in the bleak world of ice. The absurd scene ended only when his ancestral silver plummeted into a crevasse. At that moment, I realised that in the end we are fated to lose everything. That is our destiny. Our heart's cherished treasure is the mere currency of fools.

An ivory gull, heedless of our pain, soared above us in the open heaven, an immaculate creation, as pure and serene as a dove. Then after seven days, the ice split, and we dashed for freedom, fighting loose of our icy tomb like rats snatched from the maw of a tiger. Now we stagger south, crashing through the glacial seas.

We burst on through tempest and turbulence, our heavy ships submerged by vicious seas as we approach the British Isles. New dangers await us. We are still far from home, but the phantom world of the Pole has already receded in our minds.

One strange detail of the failed voyage remains lodged in my memory. The incident happened during the first flush of the expedition, when the novelty of the ice drove us all to a certain impulsiveness. It concerned one of the bolder youths from the *Carcass*, named Nelson, a cocky lad of fifteen or so. He darted like a ferret over the ice shelf, determined to find a white bear and wrestle it to the ground. He kept on joking about bringing the pelt home for his father as a hunting trophy. Then one fine day, a polar bear lurched into view. So he chased it. He fired a musket shot but his weapon jammed, rendered dumb by the extreme cold. So Nelson strode off with a companion, hoping to club the poor beast to death. I inwardly mocked the pride and folly of this youth, for everyone knows a bear can run faster, swim faster and strike harder than any man. It seemed as if a meaningless tragedy was about to unfold in front of our astonished eyes.

Luckily, his commanding officer fired a warning volley and the bear suddenly startled, slipping away into the icy sea-channel. A sheepish Midshipman Nelson retreated to the ship, to face the music from old Captain Lutwidge, but that night at rations all the men talked of the bravery of Horatio Nelson, and of nothing else. This young Nelson strikes me a young man of swagger and bravado, hammering at the door of Fortune, aching to break down the gates. I relish the sage Russian proverb my father taught me, "One fisherman always sees another from afar". He is one of my kind. I sense that the fishing season of our lives has already begun, and the bait is set. We will soon see the quality of the catch we can reel in.

The Miller's Son

*H*ave you ever heard the old tale of the Marquis of Carrabas? He was a poor miller's son in the depths of France, born to poverty, who inherited nothing except an old cat and a pair of boots. He was but a dull thing, but he had a vital ally. His cat was a street fighter, a suave talker, a honeyed hustler who soon parlayed his master into a fine princedom. He caught game to curry favour with the King of France. He cajoled a threatening ogre to transform himself into a meek mouse, and soon swallowed him whole and seized his castle. In the end, both the cat and his mute master lived off the fat of the land all of their days.

Perhaps there was a little more to the story than sheer fantasy, for smooth talking can win a young man a kingdom. Fortune seemed to dote on Dauvergne, our irrepressible young adventurer. On his first trip on HMS Flora, he alighted near St Petersburg and was granted an audience with Empress Catherine the Great. She was utterly entranced by this handsome and charming young naval officer. Legend has it she desired him for her royal service; regretfully, the loyal British subject had to refuse.

Adventure was calling Dauvergne. After his Arctic escapade, he cut his teeth early in the American wars, harrying bands of Colonial troops across Long Island. The rebel Minutemen were trained to pick off naval officers in their resplendent gold braid, but Dauvergne somehow managed to elude every bullet. Eventually he was cornered by a French fleet at Rhode Island, and burned his ship in desperation. For this sad act he was put to court-martial just as the regulations demanded, but Fate smiled again. He was honourably acquitted.

Then came the hero's magnificent call, the first turn of the screw. It all began with a curious concatenation of events. Dauvergne was appointed First Lieutenant of the "saucy Arethusa", one of the storied frigates of the Royal Navy, a plum command for an ambitious young mariner. The plot thickened, as disaster ensued. A howling storm fresh from the gates of hell sent his ship hurtling towards the lacerating rocks off the Breton coast, irretrievably wrecked. The Arethusa's hull splintered in shreds like matchwood. The half-drowned, bedraggled survivors were plucked from certain death but hauled away in chains, mere trophies of war. Dauvergne languished for months in a prison camp in Carhaix, a nondescript market town deep in the heart of Brittany. It was such a cruel fate, to be interned in a cell just a swallow's flight from his Jersey home. Winter fell.

Yet one day there wends a rumour, a whisper in the stillness of the dungeon. A decorated French officer steps in to the gaol, demanding to see the prisoner. His *golden epaulettes gleam in the shadows. The unkempt provincial gaoler is at first irascible, irritated at the confusing intrusion. The officer and his princely master bear the same name as the British prisoner. Who is summoning whom? There is a flutter of keys and voices, a disputation and perhaps a bribe.*

At last the heavy double-headed key prises open the lock. The officer introduces himself as Théophile Corret de la Tour d'Auvergne. He is a man destined to become a true Napoleonic hero, the legendary First Grenadier of France. He enters the cell like an angel sent from the void, bearing an arcane message from his master. The sullen prisoner will soon come to see that he has been touched by Providence. His family name, a mere accident of birth, will prove the golden ticket that will bring him not only freedom but also a stupendous fortune. So the next day the bedraggled prisoner is secreted out of the foul Carhaix jail and is whisked away to Paradise.

First Lieutenant Dauvergne is provided with a horse and a fine military escort. They are trudging now through dense primeval woodland, the ruined forest of Merlin where the Breton legends of Arthur still haunt the murky November days. Weak sunlight struggles down through the trees, as if falling to the black depths of the ocean. After all the long sea voyages, the raging wars and the prison hole, the boundaries of reality now seem fluid and elusive. The gentle forest muffles him like a womb. Then an apparition rises up from the lake.

The glorious illusion beckons, with towers and turrets, pinnacles and fountains. This vision in the forest is a palace. The party knocks at great oaken doors, elaborately carved and embossed in gold leaf. Then the door opens to a world of opulence beyond compare, a pleasure-dome of stupendous proportions built to satisfy the libertine tastes of the owner. He is the man whose name is the mirror, the cypher that will change everything - the Duc d'Auvergne.

To the bedraggled prisoner, the vision falls down like manna from heaven. He is ushered up a double staircase, which ascends up to a sensual, enticing paradise. Statues of cavorting Roman gods and goddesses, plump and nubile, adorn the alcoves of this fabulous baroque mansion. Pure water cascades from secret falls in the grounds and the floors are hewn in pure marble. Fires roar in great halls. Exotic birds flutter in gilded cages. Wine flows like spilt blood.

The mad king of this lavish domain is a bloated, stooped man, his liver riddled and his health shot to shreds by decades of dedicated debauchery. His habits of gluttony and sensual excess are the talk of France. His carnal desires are generously inclusive, but he nurses a special affection for Parisian showgirls. In a single year, it was rumoured that just one of his more enterprising courtesans had fleeced him out of the best part of half a million francs. Yet that is mere small change, petty cash for a prince of his stature. On the day of Dauvergne's arrival, a hundred assorted flunkeys, acolytes and liveried retainers swarm like flies over his gigantic mansion, feeding on this overflowing honeypot.

This astonishing edifice was merely d'Auvergne's pad in the country. Of course he had a town house in the best quartier of Paris, and far away lay his own proper domain, the Duchy of Bouillon. This puffed-up principality was in fact larger than Jersey, nestling along the French border, skirting the borders of the Holy Roman Empire. The Duke owed technical fealty to the kings of France but was puppet-master of his own domain. Dick Whittington, the owner of another fortunate feline, would have found much to envy here, for the streets of this fat and prosperous Walloon town seemed paved with gold. Thanks to indulgent taxes and liberal printing laws, the duchy had cornered a lucrative and privileged niche churning out half the libellous tracts of Europe. Its coffers literally bulged with loot.

Yet d'Auvergne had a problem, and one that all the treasure of his tragic kingdom could not solve. His own son was an invalid and had no hope of yielding an heir. The bloodline would die here. What use the trinkets of his Lilliputian little empire, if it was destined to fall into the hands of his detested cousins?

So he had begun a quest, to find a young man of nobility and character, who would be worthy of inheriting his domain. His first candidate was the gallant French officer who had freed Dauvergne from his prison cell, and who had already assumed the surname de la Tour d'Auvergne as a first step towards the prize. He was about to be unceremoniously jilted, for the dying Duke had found a new favourite.

The Jerseyman Philippe Dauvergne was a pitch-perfect applicant for the role: intrepid and sophisticated, dashing and perfectly fluent in French. His repertoire of beguiling tales spanned the flames of New York Harbour to the white nights of the Arctic. The same devastating charm that had melted the icy heart of the Russian Empress again strutted out on parade. The decrepit old Duc d'Auvergne desperately hankered after a son and heir, and on that dreamy night in February 1780 he finally found one.

Of course the legal process was slow. The Duke pulled strings and his friend was released. Then the exotic drama resumed on other shores. Young Dauvergne was wrecked on an obscure desert island in the Atlantic, undergoing trials of purgatory like any hero must before he obtains the glorious prize. His reward duly followed. Eventually his natural father renounced all rights and he was formally adopted. In 1791 the naval officer was proclaimed Philippe d'Auvergne, Prince-Successor to the Duchy of Bouillon. Mad King George graciously granted permission for his subject to ascend to the throne of a foreign potentate. His inheritance now seemed assured.

Philippe Dauvergne, this Jersey country boy had, through sheer chutzpah and

Fashions changed, and soon the forgotten fantasias of princelings counted for little. In 1924 the Tower was deliberately and slowly razed to the ground, brick by brick. The turrets and battlements were reduced to charred rubble. The time of the Tower had passed, and the grassy mound of La Hougue Bie returned to the patient care of the ancients. In the words of Shelley, nothing beside remains. Only the little medieval chapel clung onto the summit like a tenacious prayer.

The dream vanished at daybreak, where the deep fields of Jersey slope down on all sides from the empty hill, cascading away towards the bright horizon. The sea still glimmers in the dawn light like a whispered, tantalising promise.

The Summer Queen

Jersey 1846

The New Map of Europe

*T*he dreams of a tragic prince had died, smothered by the new map of Europe that rose from the ashes of Waterloo. His preposterous folly still perched high over Jersey, a testament to the futility of vain mortals. It would witness much more.

In the long Regency era, Jersey changed. The white fire of the industrial and agricultural revolution that had convulsed England tossed a few stray sparks to its somnolent Norman cousins. At last Town boasted a modern harbour; the new Quai des Marchands, funded in the spirit of self-reliance by the Jersey merchants themselves. Beyond the Town Church, the treacherous dunes of Helier's fishing hamlet were at last penned up behind a modern seawall. The seaport flourished. Town's urban tentacles began to creep up the shaded côtils of the parish, and a spate of new roads broke up the Jersey meadows. The residences of Rouge Bouillon and Almorah Crescent might well pale in comparison to Bath's honeycomb masterpieces, but for old Jersey these were bold statements of wealth and intent. Gas lights, the pinnacle of Regency technology, now blazed across St Helier's most exclusive streets.

Jersey remained a house sulky and divided. The reactionaries took up the symbol of the Laurel, while the progressives gathered under the banner of the Rose. Animosity between them literally grew entrenched, as floral motifs sprung up in their gardens. Their monotonous rivalry was subsumed only by the shared Jersey imperative of glorious moneymaking. The Newfoundland fisheries still churned out cash; the Englishman habitually drank himself witless on Jersey cider, and the ruthlessly overfished oyster beds of Gorey furnished London's discerning palates with exquisite and succulent morsels. After 1833, the beguiling and doe-eyed Jersey cow was perfected and bred for export: its rich milk would soon nourish half the world. Money talks, and the British pound, currency of an energetic and aggressive industrial empire, eventually ousted the traditional French coinage of the islands. The heavy gold livres tournois, the unit of account since time immemorial, fell at last into the realm of memory.

Then word came from the mainland. The house of Hanover had fallen and old King William IV had slipped away. The throne of England and the ancient dukedom of Normandy had passed to an eighteen-year old girl. Her name was Victoria. For centuries the Dukes had been revered, but as absentee landlords. Yet this young lady, bold and utterly decisive, was a very different proposition. She was determined to inspect her oldest domains at close quarters. The shock news exploded into sleepy Jersey like an anarchist's bomb.

The Queen was coming.

The Bailiff's Story: Sir John de Veulle

September 2, 1846

Queen Victoria is here and Jersey is on fire. At first she is a whispered rumour, a hope beyond daring, rising up like a mirage in the blistering heat. Then the tall arms of high promise blaze in across the horizon, as the dark silhouette of the Royal Yacht glides into full view round Noirmont. A battery of guns erupts from Fort Regent and the Island swoons as if caught in a dream. The shock is pure and electric, as magnetic and irresistible as anything Faraday can offer, and a surge of euphoric joy hares across the Island. She is the heir to Rollo and Rufus, our fabled covenant queen, come at last to grace these shores with her Presence, if only for a day. Our young and vivacious Sovereign, the pinnacle of all mortal power and beauty, will stand in our streets, smile at our children and grace our dreams.

Heaven has bestowed on us a perfect sunset to mark the arrival. The Royal Flotilla is bathed in a shimmering sea of light, a field of the cloth of gold pouring down from the setting sun. The sleek and opulent Royal Yacht, the *Victoria and Albert*, along with its siblings the *Fairy*, *Black Eagle* and the *Garland*, have cast anchor. It has been a bracing voyage down here through the surging, rock-infested channel of the Alderney Race. The sailors have gladly anchored this evening in the Great Roads, nestling close to the gentle heart of St Aubin's Bay. Colonel le Couteur escorts me to my boat, and we row out to meet the royal party, to honour their arrival and arrange our final plans.

Prince Albert is keen to see the magnificent edifice of Mont Orgueil, and so the eastern parishes will welcome the royal carriage tomorrow. As we discuss the finer details of the itinerary, Her Majesty graciously appears on deck, and expresses how she has so long anticipated touring her Island Realm for the first time. My heart leaps in my breast as if I was a young man again, and my mouth is struck parched and speechless, but a surge of the old Jersey pride roars in me. I will leave the Royal Yacht later that night as spellbound and ardent as a knight of old.

The best is yet to come, for since the word first came from Guernsey a week ago, I have chaired the Jersey committee charged with our feverish preparations. We have loosened our purse strings and thrown prudence to the wind, for Destiny calls us but once in a lifetime. Half the flowers of the Island have been culled and sacrificed at the shrine of Her Majesty's glory, and tomorrow the sheer extravagance of our Jersey welcome will be unveiled. We are at last ready to serenade our May Queen.

My Island has truly prospered from its long allegiance to the Crown. The world is charging ahead faster now than a steam locomotive, propelling Great Britain to the forefront of the world. This bold and new Victorian Age is as terrible as an army with banners, a staggering and unfurling revelation. In the past decade railways have snaked the length and breadth of Britain and we are become the workshop and envy of the world. The earth has seen nothing like it since the Roman.

Change has come, even in this bucolic Island. Scarcely a few years past, men here reckoned their wealth in the ancient French coinage of *livres tournois* and *sous*, but these days the English currency of pounds, shillings and pence circulates freely alongside the old coinage of the Island. Old folk grumble of course, but Progress must have its day. This is the spirit of the age, our brave new world of iron and railways and industry that will surely change Jersey in our new Victorian Age.

Night is falling fast now. The hillsides are glowing with a dozen furious bonfires, and some over-excited fool at Noirmont has conspired to set the entire hillside ablaze. The flames rage savage and rampant for hours, burning ferociously like a wild beacon from Norman days. We are nestling here far below in the darkness, cloaked in the sweet black oblivion of St Aubin's Bay. The immaculately liveried crew, doubtless jaded to the fervent choreography of royal welcomes, observe the fiery welcome and silently resume their duties.

As the sun swoops below Noirmont, a fairy extravaganza bursts to life under the warm moon. Every house facing the bay has been instructed to hold a gas lamp or a candle high. St Aubin's is transformed into a sparkling fantasia of yellow light.

Across the unfathomable blackness of the bay the signal shrouds of Fort Regent are illuminated, and the timber yards of the Esplanade are shining like a lighthouse, calling their Duc home. Crowds are swarming and surging on the Jersey hills, dancing and cheering in the hot night. All the fervent passions of the Laurel and Rose factions are forgotten tonight. Crowds have gathered to gawp at this spectacle in the hot night, to pledge their troth at the court of the Summer Queen. Waves of hurrahs and cheers roll in like low thunder, echoing across the long reach of the night bay.

Suddenly the sky above is drenched in light again, as a fusillade of welcoming rockets tear like meteors over the bay. The spectacle I ordered at the Fort has begun. The fireworks explode in the Victorian ether and fizzle and swivel down in frolics of scarlet, white fire and electric blue. Jersey has pulled no punches in its lavish welcome, and as a son of this Island, I stand proud.

We clamber on board the tender and start to row for shore. The royal couple are taking the night air on the deck of their yacht, feasting their eyes on the immaculate extravaganza. They smile at the dazzling rainbows of light, and I fancy I hear a peal of girlish laughter cascading over the decks.

Centuries have passed, and like a fleeting comet, the ancient light of kings has returned to blaze again in its oldest and proudest domain. Welcome here to Jersey, my glorious Sovereign. Welcome home.

Victoria's Harbour

*F*ew *in Jersey sleep that night, for the sultry air, the feverish anticipation and the delirium of the final preparations are too much. In the dark hours before sunrise, the country folk are already flooding into town, jostling and scrambling for a viewpoint, fighting for their chance to catch a glimpse of the sublime. By eight o'clock the pier seats are all taken. So desperate men are scrambling up to the boatyards and scaling up the masts of ships in the harbour. The* Iris *boasts a hastily constructed viewing platform and men gladly shinny up rigging and perch on yardarms to obtain a better view. The struggle is worth it, for they will be able to tell their children and grandchildren that on this single spellbound day, they witnessed history.*

The hot September morning finally breaks. Twenty-seven year old Queen

Victoria awakes to ripples of sunlight dancing over the luscious ultramarine blue of St Aubin's Bay. The young Queen is astounded at the exotic sight; it is surely as charming, she suggests, as the Bay of Naples. Prince Albert, no stranger to the alluring shores of the Italian Riviera, duly concurs.

The vast crowds are surging forward long before the royal party makes leisurely preparations to land. Over forty thousand loyal spectators have gathered in St Helier, the numbers swollen by visitors from Guernsey and Normandy who have flocked here for the grand occasion. They are swarming like ants on every inch of the Town Hill, milling on every rock and outcrop to hail their beloved Duke.

The waterfront is bustling with frantic preparations, even at this late hour. Wagons laden with flowers have been rolling in from the country for days, bearing boughs and blooms to construct the magnificent floral arches on every principal St Helier street. Every house here has been freshly painted or swiftly renovated, dubbed with a lick of paint or a banner of celebration. Even the most dilapidated sheds have been transformed by a fairy queen's spell into tranquil floral pagodas. St Helier has become a summer carnival of flowers, the proud capital of a world made new.

Now the States of Jersey, in the full pomp and regalia of their office, are marching out to meet their Sovereign. The hallowed mace of King Charles II, famed treasure of the Island, is paraded in honour before them. All three historic orders have come to pledge their loyal obeisance – the hooded Rectors in clerical garb, the Jurats in their magisterial robes, and the stern Constables of the twelve Parishes. A cluster of dignitaries gaggle like geese in a lavishly appointed pavilion at the pier head, specially built for the arrival of the Fairy Queen. A sumptuous furl of rich red Brussels carpet leads right down from here to the water's edge. De Gruchy's redoubtable furniture emporium has neatly excelled itself with this grand offering.

The Royal Standard of England and the arms of Jersey flutter hypnotically together above the crowds in the radiant morning. A third enormous silken flag ripples nearby, bearing a brand new name hastily unveiled in a flash of inspiration this day. The New Harbour is no more; this is 'Victoria Harbour' now.

The heat is blistering and the burning reflection of the sun on the bay is dazzling. The approaching royal barge appears just like a painted toy, a serene swan floating in on a smooth and glassy sea. As in a dream, the boat glides in to dock. The crowds are struck mute, with the people held spellbound as if in a trance. The air feels dense and heavy, as if charged with an electrical storm.

Then a beautiful young lady steps forward out of the boat. A spark of euphoria ignites the crowd and consumes them in a single explosive instant. A devastating cacophony of cheers erupts, far more deafening than any artillery volley. The primal roar of twenty thousand adoring subjects breaks like a tsunami of sound, shaking the pink granite of Jersey to its foundations and careening through the heat of the bay. Then thunder strikes high above, as heavy cannon fire blaze down their loyal salute from the heights of Mount Bingham. The dream is made flesh, and the carnival frenzy has begun. The atmosphere is delirious and contagious, and little Jersey is swept up in the sheer pandemonium of joy.

So this, at last, is royalty. Her Majesty is sublime, sporting an elegant green and white silk dress, a pretty lilac scarf and a summer bonnet as pure as the driven snow. Prince Albert, for his part, is dashing and gallant as ever in a uniform of lavender trousers, black coat and white silk waistcoat emblazoned with the ancient and heroic Order of the Garter. Then Colonel le Couteur ushers the Duke forward to receive the homage of Miss Le Maistre, the daughter and only heir of the Seigneur of St Ouen's Manor. His forebears hosted the fugitive King Charles and the fanciful legend tells they fought at Duke William's right hand on the bloody field of Hastings. Today this first fief of the Island has come to renew its ancient allegiance to the Crown.

Then a perfect troop of ladies draped in purest lily white, like a flock of vestal virgins, rushes forward to welcome their May Queen. Her path is strewn with flowers; her feet dance lightly on the plush Brussels rug that leads from the dock up to the royal pavilion. The military bands of the 81st and Town Militia, in burnished military scarlet, strike up the National Anthem. As Sir John de Veulle steps up to commence his speech of welcome, a surge of feverish optimism wells up in another thunderous round of huzzahs and applause. The storm breaks over Jersey.

The Sovereign's Story: Queen Victoria

We are truly enchanted by Jersey. The joyful welcome and gay atmosphere of this pretty little Island is contagious. Our reception in Guernsey was overwhelming and now her sister is proving her loyalty burns just as proudly. We awoke to a beautiful morning today as the sun rose high over the bay, which really is as splendid as Naples. Bertie came on deck in his fine military dress and the sailors heartily cheered him as he surveyed the deck. He made some fine etchings of the Jersey coast last night as we passed all these charming little beaches and sandy coves. It is always a joy to spend time with my husband here on the Yacht, away from the claustrophobia and responsibilities of Court.

We set off in the *Fairy* and then transferred to another barge for our approach. From our little boat, it seemed as if every hillside, every house and every ship was crowded with men and women, all of them cheering and raising their hats as we drew nearer. We pulled alongside the stairs of the newly christened Victoria Harbour, and here the ladies of the Island came to pay their respects.

The States paid a fine and loyal address, and we then embarked on a circuit of St Helier's, the charming principal town. Our horses are dressed in immaculate red ribbons, in the style of our finest state occasions in London. It is a lovely procession. The joy of the Jersey people is delightful, and they ensured that so many beautiful flowers were strewn in our path. Of course they have had longer to make preparations than the good inhabitants of St Peter Port, but that does not in the least detract from the effusive nature of their welcome. My A.D.C., Col. Le Couteur, is of course a proud Jerseyman and a gold mine of local facts – he tells me that the local tongue, although it seems rather like French to me, is in fact a very ancient dialect dating from Norman times. I do hope it will be safely preserved, just like the Welsh tongue, for many generations to come. As we passed the Market, I even caught sight of a brace of French fisherwomen, clad in ancient Norman dress as if they had just stepped out of the Bayeux Tapestry. They duly doffed their bonnets in homage and I made sure to smile and greet them.

As we passed the hospital, Col. Le Couteur pointed out the invalids and the orphans who in their rags had come to see the procession. "I beg your pardon", he said, "but the poor as well as the rich have come to greet your Majesty". I waved to them all. "And the little children too, please Your Majesty", he added, and I made sure that I bowed to each and every one of the dear little orphans.

He then showed me the very spot where that gallant patriot Peirson fell in honour over sixty-five years ago. This was the last time that the French have threatened Jersey; even wily old Napoleon did not dare venture here. The States had been following us on foot all the way through the town, and seeing them somewhat red in the face from the exertion, I dispensed with their gracious company. We drew up outside Government House, but poor old General Gibbs, the Governor, is very ill and sadly unable to receive us. So our carriage turned in salute in the driveway, and then we progressed up a steep hill and broke out into open country.

The Jersey countryside is lush and green, with magical orchards stretching everywhere. It is exceedingly picturesque, although it does feel somewhat deserted and empty compared to England. I questioned Colonel le Couteur on the emptiness of the fields, and he explained that all the people had come to town especially for my visit. He also mentioned that potatoes are the principal crop of the Island, and I was most reassured to hear that the crops are holding up well despite the terrible blight that is affecting so many other parts of the realm. Then we pressed on through some charming lanes, where the branches of the elm-trees form a pretty natural arch over our heads. The curious old Tower of La Hougue Bie looms over the fields here like a relic of Gothic times.

We are now making directly for the ancient Jersey castle of Mont Orgueil, which I proudly learn has never surrendered to an enemy of England. Bertie is very keen to survey the battlements and spy the French coast, which hangs so bright on the horizon, and appears almost close enough to touch.

The coach clatters on through the narrow and leafy lanes of the Island. I can only wish the journey was a little shorter, for it is a very hot day, and this is by no means the mild and clement weather of our English summers. The Jersey sun is terribly fierce and I am beginning to feel more than a little faint.

The Keys to the Castle

*T*he *ancient Ceremony of the Keys is about to begin. Colonel Dixon strides forward to the Castle Gate and demands entrance. The stern Wardens refuse, for they have sworn to yield only to their lawful Sovereign.*

A tiny, dainty figure descends from the landau. She flits with the lightness of a young girl, but carries an authority that can move the world. As she approaches, the Wardens fall to their knees in a theatrical show of fealty. Then they surrender the Keys, perfectly tied with a silk ribbon. Victoria smiles and returns them to her Colonel Dixon. At last, the bleak and savage fortress that even defied Du Guesclin throws its gates wide open.

This is only the beginning. Albert energetically storms to the summit of the battlements, wanting to explore every nook and cranny of the great Castle. Lord Palmerston huddles up conspiratorially with the Bailiff, no doubt discussing the secret military plans to construct an immense naval base in St Catherine's Bay. They survey the sparkling turquoise horizon, and in their mind's eye, a vast double breakwater already glimmers like a scorpion's pincer, projecting British sea power towards the heart of Europe.

The young queen stays on the Grand Battery, her gaze skipping over the glittering horizon and the ravishing sea. She casts a fresh eye over the great shipyards and booming oyster fleets of Gorey, and the verdant fields of St Martin. She asks for a telescope, and so Le Couteur scurries off to procure one. She surveys the twin spires of Coutances Cathedral, glistening like needles on the horizon. They say it was used as a grain store during the French Revolution, before becoming a desecrated Temple of Reason. Queen Victoria shudders, then tilts the telescope and thirstily drinks in the rest of the gorgeous panorama.

Hers is the restless energy of the future, demanding to see further and faster. The young Victorian age is exploding like a supernova, a kaleidoscope of colour and opportunity and ambition. Britain is steaming forward like a freight train, smashing through the cholera and famine of the Hungry Forties to begin its rise to greatness. Northern cities have already sucked in hundreds of thousands and swallowed up villages and fields, in a dirty and smoky vision of hell. Yet they are churning out a vast and bewildering array of goods that is cementing British power and prestige across the world. An invisible web of Free Trade and Progress is binding the earth closer, and Jersey is drawn inexorably to the centre.

These days the exquisite Gorey oysters wash up on the City of London's finest dinner plates; they are pure aquatic gold. The little packet boats that leave the new Gorey Pier and steam to France carry the gospel of Free Trade. The world is shrinking; this very year, pioneering British technologists have launched the world's first Electric Telegraph Company. Since the days of Babel, mankind has been scattered, torn apart by the tyranny of distance, but now the magic of instant communication has arrived. Jersey's long isolation, at the mercy of tides and storms since time immemorial, is about to end forever.

The revels now are over and the summer dream is fading fast. The Lord Chamberlain signs the Visitor's Book on behalf of the Queen, and dates it: September 3, 1846. The ink dries quickly in the September heat, as the royal party speeds back past Prince's Tower and races for the docks. Jersey shakes off the stupor of adoration and the crowds drift back into their ordinary lives.

The lively young monarch has slipped away, her quicksilver mind darting now over new terrain and new horizons. The air she breathes seems charged with possibility, and no Jerseyman will forget this day.

The Queen is gone. She leaves only the sunlight dancing over the bay, as bright and fleeting as a lover's caress.

Race Meeting at Grouville Common, 25 July 1849 (painted 1850)
Philip John Ouless (1817-1885)
Courtesy of the Jersey Heritage Collections

A Revolutionary in Jersey: Karl Marx

Karl Marx by John Mayall (circa 1870)
© National Portrait Gallery, London

Mrs Langtry (1853 - 1929) by Edward John Poynter (1878)

Florence Boot - A Jersey Pioneer
© The Alliance Boots Archive & Museum Collection

Charlie Chaplin by Alexander ('Alick')
Penrose Forbes Ritchie, 1926 (Detail).
© National Portrait Gallery, London

The first aeroplane to land in Jersey - photograph by A Laurens (1912)
© Société Jersiaise Photographic Archive, Jersey, SJPA/034990

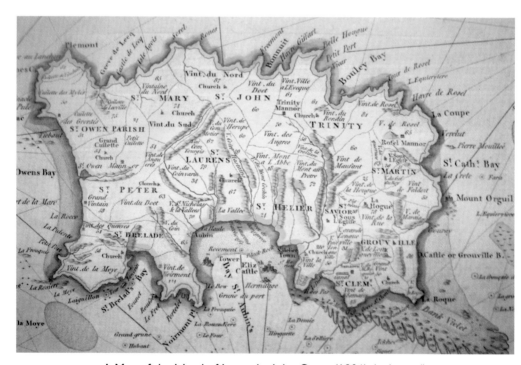

A Map of the Island of Jersey by John Carey (1806) (coloured)
La Hougue Bie is shown as "La Hogue" and Gorey Castle as "Mount Orguil"
Courtesy of www.albion-prints.com

Victorian Sunset

The Revolutionary's Story – Karl Marx

Hotel de l'Europe, St Helier

16 August 1879

D o not be fooled. I am not just another harmless old man sipping his tea, gently idling his time away in the starched dining suite of the Hotel de l'Europe. The hustle and clatter of Mulcaster Street beyond are deeply muffled here through the thick double doors, and I am nestled closely as if in a womb.

I sagely ruffle my stained fingers through my thick grey frieze of a beard, stirring my tea, mulling over the latest signs of this dying age. I am over in Jersey with my daughter Tussy to seek refuge from the scourge of bronchitis and the foul London fogs. She enjoys sea bathing, and is dipping today down at St Clement. I am, for my part, content to sit and brood. No-one knows my name here, and not even the witless concierge can spell it aright: 'Dr Marcks and lady'.

The trip down from Waterloo Station was uneventful, even if the sea crossing was rougher than usual in this limpid and rain-lashed summer. Our train was suitably sleek and fast, charged with the fierce energy of Victorian Britain, the bottled black lightning of capitalism that has transformed our world. I know the face of my age: an earth tamed and shrunk, factories spewing out supernormal profits; concentrated wealth sloughed off from the servile backs of the dumb masses.

The Island has changed so much in these last days of the old order. Jersey today is crowded with the worst kind of Englishman: the *petit bourgeois* with too much money and delusions to match. The island is plagued these days with a swarm of entrepreneurs, hawkers and hucksters, all of them scratching out a living from the underbelly of this rotten carcass. Standards have slipped; we left the Trafalgar Hotel in St Aubin because the monotonous broiled lamb and mutton were enough to turn me a reluctant vegetarian. I prefer blood.

My comrade Engels was all too right when he wrote to me from Jersey in 1874: the place is indeed crawling with 'philistines, commercial clerks and volunteers, and snobs'. As he noted, Jersey is being shorn like a mute sheep of its original Norman heritage. "Jersey has changed a great deal since we were there together. A vast amount of building, elegant villas, big hotels – high, almost English prices in them… The French language is disappearing fast, even the country children now speak almost nothing but English without any French accent, nearly all of them".

That is the power of capitalism for you: global, unifying, as incessant and relentless as the tide. History of course, being as inevitable as clockwork, will revolve. I spy the frail machinery propping up the brittle façade of Empire. I have already prophesied the next act in the drama.

It is beyond doubt now that this Victorian economic age is moving through systemic depressions and crises, each one proving more crippling than the last. A final crisis of capital is coming and this will rip off the veil. I am an old man and the radical flame of my youth is dim, but I care not, for I am a mere vehicle of clay and dust. I already spy the first fingers of dawn, the godless utopia of a new earth under an empty heaven. But first there will be fire.

I observe my fellow Jersey diners as I would a flock of birds: waddling, haughty, all strut and show. They flaunt their fading plumage in the evening light. Decorum and pretension reigning triumphant to the end, like the rites of a dying swan. These graceful idiots are blind to the change that is to come, for the hour is already late, and the sands of history are already slipping away beneath their fingers. This hotel and the continent of Europe it honours, are living on borrowed time.

"The Hotel de l'Europe is excellent, and one day we must go here together, *toute la famille*", I wrote to my family last night. I relish the discreet service; the starched impeccable linen; the veneer of bourgeois elegance, the diners sumptuously feasting on the edge of a volcano. I devour my steak, relishing the faint tang of blood.

Do not be fooled, Europe. Your house will burn.

Victorian Jersey

*I*t is sunset in high August, at the very apogee of the Victorian age. The sun completes its glorious circuit west across St Aubin's Bay and subsides ever lower, its rays finally splintering across the primeval dark green slopes of the Noirmont headland. Ever since the volcano of Krakatoa violently split its head open, the weather has been foul, but the sunsets everywhere, as if in compensation, have been magnificent.

This evening the skies are daubed as pink as the imperial globes on sale in De Gruchy's flourishing retail emporium. Abroad, the brisk business of British global hegemony continues; for in Vancouver it is noon; in Auckland, it is daybreak. These twelve ancient parishes of Jersey, among the most ancient possessions of the Crown, are now mere grains of sand amongst the millions of square miles of prairie and desert that have been cajoled, subjugated and forged together into the greatest Empire in human history. Little Jersey has by accident found itself at the threshold of the world's sole superpower, a peculiar gateway to the sprawling and bloated imperium whose financial and industrial tentacles grasp the globe.

So Jersey is flush these days with a new tribe of settlers, a certain breed of portly and dyspeptic Englishman, clad in garish military regalia and boasting a dull retinue of absurdly overdressed children and sullen servants in tow. These arrivals are the Colonels and Admirals, a parade of Imperial functionaries washed up from the hot shores of Ceylon and Aden, released from tedious tours of duty in the wilds of the Bight of Benin or the Cape Colony. These men have eyes fogged by an excess of pink gin and white tropical sun, and consciences dulled by their mediocre careers dispensing the brutality and blessings of imperial rule. They are lured here to Jersey by the gentle summer climate and a gratifying absence of income tax, always a boon when maintaining the fragile illusion of bourgeois respectability on the back of a military pension. So their purses bulge with gold sovereigns bearing the unseeing head of the Empress of India, freshly rolled from the Imperial mints of Sydney or London. Suffocating in the stifling etiquette and formality of bourgeois Jersey life, their days revolve around the Lieutenant-Governor's social circle and the Regiment. These old fossils slowly stagnate under the Jersey sun, drinking to numb the memories of their glory days. Jersey has become the island where, under the rows of token palm trees, the petty potentates of the British Empire come to die.

The old Norman ways are fading fast, for Progress and Industry have shrunk the world like a withered balloon. From London Waterloo, the bombastic gateway to the Imperial City itself, the voyager may take a fast train as late as 9pm that charges down to Southampton Docks. Passengers are then transferred directly to a waiting steamship and arrive at St Helier waterfront in a matter of hours. From the Weighbridge railway terminal, the splendid Jersey Railway will transport passengers along the delightful curve of St Aubin's Bay. Just this month a direct connection has been opened to take them up the cutting to the magnificent headland of Corbière, where a fist of granite rock punches the bitter Atlantic. Of course, these days Nature is domesticated at the foot of science. Some eleven years ago a towering white lighthouse was constructed here and its light blazes across the bay. The terrible haunt of black crows is now just another tourist attraction. The treacherous western shoals that instilled fear for centuries, have been rendered toothless.

In one generation, science has tamed the world. The very first pillar boxes in the Empire were established right here in St Helier in 1852, when Vaudin & Son produced four octagonal olive-green ornaments for David Place, New Street, Cheapside and St Clement's Road. The humble technology of the postage stamp has of course spread like wildfire. Just six years later, the first telegraph service opened in the Island. That fabulous new invention of Mr Bell, the telephone, will surely arrive here before the decade is out.

With such excellent connections, Jersey is rapidly transforming itself into a tourist haven, a holidaymaker's pleasure dome. Its charming southern climes seem a world away from the squalor, smog and black rain of Victorian industrial cities. The fortifying sea air is an ideal tonic for Englishmen choked by bronchitis, the plague of the modern age. Spying an opportunity, Mr William Briggs of Rouge Bouillon is ardently promoting the "Royal Jersey Medicated Cigarettes for Asthma and Bronchitis". His press advertisements carry the encouraging testimony that "these cigarettes have been thoroughly tested for upwards of five years, and have gained an increasing reputation". The precise nature of this "reputation" remains unelaborated.

So a brace of smart hotels has opened in St Helier to pamper the more discerning class of bronchially afflicted holidaymaker. In the years since the spectre of a certain snide and superannuated revolutionary haunted the Hotel de l'Europe, the Island's tourist attractions have flourished. This summer, tourists are flocking up to the Troglodyte Caves at Five Oaks, which boast a stately pleasure palace worthy of the Orient. The entrepreneurial local brick-maker Mr Champion has laid out here an array of enticing pavilions, groves and sinister gothic statues. In the cooler months, the ice rink proves a compelling draw to idle away the hours.

The tourist in this Indian summer of Victoriana is advised to press on to nearby

Prince's Tower, to survey the Island from the gothic fantasia perched high above the old barrow of La Hougue Bie in St Saviour. From its utmost turrets, the northern vistas unfurl like a rich velvet carpet. The whole Island appears spread out at one's feet like an extensive park thickly planted with trees, cut with twisting valleys and sunlit uplands. It is an easy stroll from here up to the medieval bastion of Gorey, perhaps taking a charming detour past the secluded watermills and bountiful meadows of delightful Queen's Valley, named of course in honour of Her Majesty's visit back in the Forties.

The more athletically minded holidaymaker can hire tricycles from Jersey Cycle Works, to be found just four doors down from the Town Hall. As the Island's orchards give way to the marvellous new kidney potato, duly honoured with the appellation of Jersey Royal, there is no excuse for any visitor to retire to bed hungry.

A scan of the newspapers this month in the damp August of 1885 reveals the restless energy and optimism of Victorian Britain that is remaking the world and the Island in its image. Scorning the old country patois, this month's British Press and Jersey Times reveals an increasingly Anglophone Island drawn ever more tightly into the Empire's orbit. The Jersey newspaper's editorial, stoking the coals of its reactionary readership, fulminates against the manifold treacheries of Gladstone's Liberal government. The Grand Old Man has overseen a "dismal series of Gladstonian failures, going on as they did from worse to worse, through shocking scenes of vacillation, disaster and bloodshed till they culminated in that supreme crime – the abandonment of GORDON". It is of course only seven months since that human whirlwind of Victorian moral fervour, General Gordon, was savagely butchered in Khartoum.

So to fortify grieving spirits, this month at the Royal Hall in St Helier, George Poole will be hosting an Acme Concert Party with bands and a spectacular Diorama to celebrate the "Grand Achievements of Our Naval and Military Heroes". It is little wonder that the glamorous prospects and wide horizons of Empire will lure many a Jersey lad. For the young and adventurous, emigration by steamship to the "young and promising Colony of Queensland" is advertised for a mere £7. Mr P. B. Mourant of 10 Bond Street, St Helier will provide further details on request.

A more conventional career path lies in the staid drudgery of Victorian domestic service. "Wanted: a boy of good character to make himself generally useful", reads one such notice. Meanwhile, the rich owner of Beaulieu in Gorey advertises for a "Housemaid, about 25 years old, must be willing, of good character".

Yet the first stirrings of social change are starting to open up opportunities undreamed of by previous generations. The spanking new Beresford Library now boasts ten thousand volumes to cater for the voracious appetites of a newly literate

Island. The Jersey press is full of bright advertisements for the newly opened Jersey Ladies College, which is excelling under the beady auspices of the formidable Miss Roberts, late of Newnham College, Cambridge. Three of her pupils sent up to London University examinations passed in the First division, and one obtained the First Gilchrist exhibition of £40 per annum, tenable for two years.

This week, a jocular editorial in the British Press and Jersey Times blames the new invention of the perambulator for raising an Amazonian generation of young women. Young girls these days are born to be "independent-minded, and to know a good deal better than their mothers, and to go forth on the errand of subjugating the male sex with more confidence". The sorry sight of nursemaids dawdling with their infant charges in front of drapers and milliners is a clear cause of conspicuous consumption in later life; "We must not blame Ethel and Isabel, Florrie and Lillie", the article continues, "but must put blinkers on the maid's offside".

For even in the teeth of the depression of the early 1880s, the grand age of the St Helier department store has dawned. Just two years ago De Gruchy's fabulous retail emporium installed the latest mesmeric marvel – electric lights! Now well-to-do customers may stride in glorious illumination beneath its 240-foot covered walkway reminiscent of Piccadilly's iconic Burlington Arcade. "Money makes money", reads one advertisement in the British Press and Jersey Times promising to double your money in stocks and shares. Next year a sudden and savage banking crisis will shake the Island to its foundations; but in the summer of 1885 the prosperous Jerseyman has never had it so good.

Even as the Island changes, the increasingly quaint and archaic institutions of Jersey soldier on. The Constable of St Helier helpfully advises that swimming naked is prohibited within 50 yards of the shore after 8 am, and persons so offending will be prosecuted. Meanwhile, the sad machinery of parochial justice continues to churn out its roster of indigent, unfortunate victims.

This week, the Constable of St Saviour's charged a Mrs Richardson with the wanton crime of neglecting to maintain her daughter, Nelly. "Prisoner pleaded poverty as an excuse, alleging she had not the means to support the child. Her only means of existence seemed to be prostitution". This delinquent mother was duly sentenced to four days' imprisonment. In other news, a drunken husband who assaulted his wife and broke the furniture in his home has been fined the punitive sum of one pound sterling, with the alternative of four days in gaol should his funds prove inadequate.

So this is Jersey in August 1885, a high Victorian chiaroscuro of wealth and destitution, light and darkness, frenetic energy and indolent pleasure. The steamships dock and depart like clockwork, depositing a fresh rotation of *characters at the foot of the looming Fort Regent. This month, one broken man from Nottingham trudged off the steamship at St Helier's bustling harbour. He felt the sting of poverty in his bones, having wandered barefoot as a child to pluck herbs for his mother's little medicine shop. This lonely toiler has given the best years of his life to build the business into a little chain of dispensing chemists, but now the bill has arrived. Years of backbreaking labour have wrecked his health. In desperation, his sister beseeched him to take his first ever holiday, in the southern pleasure paradise of Jersey, and he reluctantly agreed.*

The man of sorrows was Jesse Boot, and right here in St Helier, he was about to fall in love.

The Bookseller's Story: Florence Boot

Villa Millbrook, St Lawrence
August 1934

I am and will always be a Jersey shop girl at heart, and nothing that has happened to me since will ever change that simple fact. That is why I always say to the girls on the front line: be proud of yourselves, work hard and remember that serving customers is a noble calling. I know that is true because I am one of you. You might just see this old lady, whisked around in a black Rolls-Royce, dispensing gifts to charities and tottering around as one of the great and the good. But look behind the mask and remember that I was once like you, young and free and with a wonderful life stretching out ahead of me to live.

So who am I? Well if you know St Helier, you will know Grove Place, over near Burrard Street. They say you should never ask a lady her age, but, whisper it softly, I was born here in the hot July summer of 1863, a date so long ago now that it feels as if it should be carved in a medieval arch. Those were the days long before the war, long before the motorcar, when Jersey was just a simple and beautiful place.

I grew up here like any other ordinary Jersey girl, working in my Father's shop. That was of course William Rowe's, Bookseller, on King Street, and we prided ourselves on the finest stock and most attentive service on the Island. My earliest memory is of toddling around the counters at my Father's side, helping him with the books and the till receipts and wrapping the tomes in paper bags for the clients.

Don't listen to the snobs and the critics, for I have never forgotten my roots. My beloved Father always impressed upon me that labour in a shop is a high and noble calling. When I was a young girl, I taught Sunday School at St James's Church in Town, and I always made sure the children knew that being polite and courteous was the best way we could spread God's love in this wicked world. And He soon blessed me richly more than I could ask or imagine.

I was twenty-three when I first set eyes on my dearest, beloved Jesse. I had found a man of faith, noble and strong, with a love of commerce. I have never known anyone as devoted to his business and his God, and yet he was missing one vital ingredient – a loving wife. We obtained our Special Licence at the Deanery (as dear Jesse was Nottingham-born and not of this Duchy) and were married forthwith.

There was little time for a honeymoon. I was soon working eight to ten hours in the business along with Jesse – we truly made this enterprise our own. Boots the Chemist flourished from the sweat of our own labour – through honest toil, day after day, come rain or shine. I have always loved fashion and style, and I soon moulded the somewhat workaday Boots stores into my own personal taste. Why after all should a customer buy their medicines in a bland shop when they could saunter through a mock-Tudor country house? I encouraged Jesse to think on a grander scale, taking on the department stores at their own game, stocking a great variety of perfumes, opening cafés to refresh weary shoppers.

As a bookseller's daughter, I have always loved books, and I simply wanted to give our customers, many of modest means, the same opportunities that I had enjoyed as a child growing up. So I established the Boots Booklovers' Library, which soon flourished. Today they lend 35 million books a year – perhaps my proudest achievement of all. In such a way, my Father's spirit lives on.

I have never lost my love for Jersey. Even our home in Nottingham was christened St Helier, and as soon as circumstances allowed we purchased a home here. For one birthday my beloved Jesse bought me a delightful sandy bay, Beauport, to be our own private Eden on the south coast. In summer, it is heavenly here, where the pristine aquamarine waters lap into a sandy cove below a carpet of green gorse. This is our family's refuge and inner sanctum, our personal paradise. We eventually moved from our house at The Grove to another delightful residence – Villa Millbrook, a rambling mansion nestling in the cosy shelter of Mont Felard, surveying the immaculate blue vistas of St Aubin's Bay.

Our decades of toil eventually brought us vast and unforeseen wealth, but I have little time or inclination for the leisured life of the aristocrat. Indolence has always been my greatest enemy, along with that patronising old-fashioned nonsense that seeks to set a ceiling on what young women can achieve. I firmly believe that the aspiring modern woman should seize every opportunity in the business world of today. Let the 'shop girl' always be a badge of pride, not a mark of shame. I constantly engaged girls for the higher departments of our business – roles where they could manage both stores and people. The intelligent and educated girl would do better to avoid a frivolous life of tango teas and daylight bridge parties and instead seek a career in industry that fully employs her talents. One of my chief joys in life is the knowledge that we have been able to supply a good wage and a proper career in business to so many girls who otherwise would have struggled in a hostile world.

I am not going to relent in either my beliefs or my giving, just because age has crept up on me and I am left here alone again. My latest project will see to that. You see, ever since that awful day when the skies wept, when my beloved and tormented Jesse left us, I have dreamed of a fitting and fine memorial to the memory of my husband, one of England's finest men. The work is proceeding apace. You have doubtless heard of the reputation of my good friend, M. René Lalique. He is justly famed across Europe, as a maestro in glass, an acclaimed artist whose exquisite pieces are cherished by kings. Have you seen his fantastic fountains, embellished with soaring birds, which shine floodlit, surging like waterfalls over the Champs-Élysées? The man is truly a Renaissance master, born again for our time.

We were enjoying coffee at Villa Springland in Cannes one evening when the notion came to mind, and I can scarcely think of a finer tribute to my beloved husband. M. Lalique is going to decorate a weary old church near my home. St Matthew's is an unassuming Victorian chapel of ease perched on the Millbrook road, but we are going to change it forever.

Villa Millbrook has been a hive of activity. It sometimes feels as if Mr Grayson and his team of architects have taken up permanent residence in my drawing room, bustling in on a daily basis with models and plans and details for my personal approval.

We have already chosen the floral motif, the pure Jersey lily, which is also a symbol of our Lord. The carpets will be of the richest blue, for I think that colour is very restful and beautiful and will bring peace to so many. As for the glass decoration itself, I was privileged to review the photographs from M. Lalique's recent Paris exposition. The angels are sublime creations, poised between earth and heaven, hanging before us like shards of divine ice. Their bodies pulse with the white fire of electricity. The look in their eyes cuts to the root of my soul.

My mind wanders, as an old lady's is sometimes wont to do. My story began in sunlight, so it is right that it will end in the shimmering vistas of Lalique's Arctic ice.

Now it is the long lost summer's day when it all began. I am the Jersey shop girl that I always have been, and the world is still young and full of heart-breaking promise. I have rung up the tills for the last time this week, after six days of diligent toil for Father. It is the forlorn Sabbath again and we are solemnly praying when the door opens to our Sunday assembly.

How could I fail to sneak a glance as the dark and mysterious stranger strides in? He seems so solemn, as if he is burdened by the weight of the world, but there is grace in his step, and a supreme gentleness in his careworn face. He glances over and his eyes shine at me, warm, generous and bright. Everything has already been said, and everything has been done. I have found my pearl beyond price.

I smile at Jesse and I never look back.

The Jersey Kitten

*T*he touching love story of Florence Rowe and Jesse Boot is one of Jersey's great Victorian romances. The Glass Church at Millbrook stands as their sublime and perpetual memorial. Yet the most celebrated Jersey girl of the Victorian age was no modest and pious bookseller's daughter.

Her name was Emilie, and her father was in fact the Dean of Jersey, a man of impeccable social standing and incorrigibly philandering habits. Young Lillie grew up at his old rectory in St Saviour, a feral kitten scrapping and japing with her six tomcat brothers. This coquettish young lady married in haste, snaring the debonair Edward Langtry, whose chief appeal to his new bride was arguably his magnificent eighty foot racing yacht. Then Lillie Langtry threw herself into the libertine whirlwind of London life with all the thirst and innocent recklessness of youth.

Doors opened. Crowds drooled. The Prince of Wales, a man with a seasoned eye for emerging talent, soon came calling at her boudoir.

The legend of the Jersey Lily was born.

Episode 11

Mortal Beauty

From London 1876 to Texas 1904

The Poet's Story – Oscar Wilde

"I am going to meet the loveliest woman in Europe"
Oscar Wilde

London, 1876

I am wandering by day and night through the dirty streets of London, looking for her. The miasma and smog of the Victorian metropolis chokes me, coating me with grime as I traverse the foul shambles and gutters of this dark city. Eyes are watching me everywhere. Shadowy figures leer and sneer at my flamboyant attire; at my bright floral waistcoat; the dashing white cravat pinned to my black frock coat by a single glowing amethyst. It is all part of the show, the myth that I am weaving around her as surely as a bulbous spider in his web, poised atop these filigree threads of exquisite beauty.

I clutch in my hands a simple gift for my beloved. It is a single glistening Jersey lily, freshly plucked from the flower stall at Covent Garden. It is as innocent, soft and beguiling as that iconic visage that haunts my waking dreams. The scoffers call me a mere dilettante, a preening wastrel, a pathetic *flâneur*. To the philistine, I must seem a vulgar exhibitionist shamelessly cavorting in the limelight. Yet none of these men have understood the true shape and pattern of mortal beauty. They have not yet beheld Lillie Langtry.

My lily is held for her alone. I have dedicated my life to the pursuit of beauty, the soft touch the sublime, and in her I have finally found my prize. I wail my devotion to every bystander and weep for shame. The crowds watch me as if I am deranged, a walking folly. "There goes that bloody fool Oscar Wilde", mutters one provocateur. "It is extraordinary how soon one gets known in London", I smartly retorted, and killed that critic stone dead.

For she is my Aphrodite, and I cry her worship all the way back to my bachelor quarters off the Strand. Lillie is my Queen of the Night, as radiant as Athena, as alluring as Sarah Bernhardt. Her sheer genius is her beauty. Yet who is this Mrs Langtry, and how has she wreaked such fierce and utter devotion in the hearts of men?

She rose like Venus from the foam, a rare jewel of grace chipped from the rough granite of her homeland. She was born Emilie Le Breton, they say, a Dean's daughter from the Channel Island of Jersey, best known for its lowing cows and sturdy potatoes. From this unpromising turf, and after a marriage into minor money, she burst like a hurricane upon the London season. Suddenly she was the talk of this town. Her alabaster shoulders; her divine chin, her strikingly short hair; she was an angel clad in a single black dress. Men were stupefied and their wives could merely seethe and cringe. Before long great artists were scrambling to idolise her, her photographs were hawked on every street corner; men would scramble onto chairs or queue for hours merely to catch a passing glimpse of perfection.

Her Jersey compatriot Millais soon charted her course into the discreet echelons of high society. He bestowed on her the sobriquet of the "Jersey Lily". The legends say that long ago a ship bearing exotic bulbs from Cape Town was wrecked on that island's shores, and soon a beautiful brace of lilies flowered on the shoreline. Now she too has been plucked from the obscurity of a distant realm and been transplanted in London's fertile soil.

I first stumbled across her glory at a sitting, where my young friend Miles was sketching her. He used to immortalise a bevy of Professional Beauties in the haven of his studio, but these days they are all unemployed. Lillie has subsumed them like the rising sun. Now every moneyed banker and titled plutocrat in England is drooling over her. Wealthy men fête her with jewellery and tempt her with favours. They long to hawk her about London like a hunting trophy. I see their clawing eyes, the fevered lust burning beneath the straitjacket of their refined manners and their courtly charm. These men are corpulent predators who would simply ruin her innocence and tear her to pieces.

Whereas, I simply adore her and kiss the very ground where she treads. I put it as best I could in my trifling verse, dedicated to "Helen, formerly of Troy, now of London". Helen of Troy has returned to earth, shaking off the dust of centuries, breaking out of the tomb of decay and flouncing out into a glorious, exultant resurrection. The star that first blazed on the Trojan battlements shines again.

Heaven's sweet perfection has descended, to cavort and joust with us mere mortals and burn as radiant and gorgeous as the sunflower. The fabled Hellenic Queen of yore has returned again to bewitch and beguile the world of men.

I am reclining languorously tonight in my chambers, surrounded by the finest blue china, in halls draped in thick Grecian rugs, bedazzled and fixated by the lodestone of her beauty. A portrait of the divine Lillie sits on an easel in my room, like a pagan shrine. Her face was once emblazoned on the ancient coins of Syracuse; now it shines upon our own sanctimonious and suffocating age.

Long ago I vowed in my soul to devour every fruit of the tree of knowledge, to gorge myself on its plump and joyous spoil. Surely I have now beheld its finest flower. I am writing plays in her honour. One night I even slept on her doorstep, an ingrate humbled only to sup at the exquisite feet of the Jersey Lily. Her inebriated buffoon of a husband, a man who commits the cardinal sin of being tedious even after a brace of whiskies, stumbled over me. He kicked me into touch like a dog, accusing me of all sorts of mad calumnies.

My own piteous life is one of rented rooms and lost loves, a gnawing dejection that never lets me rest. Life seems an ever accumulating trail of losses, a recklessly gambled debt; a lost wager. Only in the contemplation of mortal beauty can I can find peace for my soul.

Lillie Langtry is my rapture, my incarnation, my line of beauty. Illusion, they say, is the first of all pleasures. I am the proud Apostle of the Lily and if this be dreaming, may I never wake.

The Beauty's Story – Lillie Langtry

"I would rather have discovered Mrs Langtry than have discovered America".

Oscar Wilde (attributed)

The American West, 1883

Last night I was dreaming again of home. The images were so incredibly vivid. I was larking again in our old rectory at St Saviour, waiting for my father the Dean to return from some urgent business in Town. The air was heavy with high summer.

I was running wild and free around the great stone cider press in the courtyard, jostling with my brothers and smiling in the warmth of the gentle Jersey sun. O happy childhood days! The memories trickled back from this honeyed lost world, long before this cascade of fame and champagne and pearls swept me away forever.

Those were simpler, larrikin days. We would rampage in the streets and steal brass doorknockers. At night we would drape ourselves in white sheets and lurk in the graveyard, scaring the living daylights out of the local bumpkins stumbling back from the tavern. So in my mind's eye I was laughing myself hoarse, japing and prancing again in the sweet sunset of the Jersey summer, when I was jolted from my pleasant reverie by the loud whistle of a steam engine. I smile as I wake.

How the world has changed. Our glorious steam folly, the *Lalee*, is rapidly gathering pace across the empty desert. The gossipmongers in the press speculate that this luxurious rail barge has cost half a million dollars, and to be fair I could trade it tomorrow for a neat little street in Knightsbridge. Yet that wouldn't be half as much fun.

It has been a glorious adventure over here in the Promised Land. I dreaded that first tedious rat-infested voyage on the SS *Arizona*, but the frightful sixteen-day transit was soon forgotten just as soon as the bright lights of the Manhattan skyline winked into view off our starboard bow.

So when our ship docked in New York City at half past four on a chilly October morning, my gallant friend Oscar was among the first of my admirers to meet me. He really hadn't changed one bit – still dressed in his famously flamboyant outfit of green fur-trimmed coat, gaudy tie and an unbuttoned shirt revealing his manly chest. He proffered me an armful of lilies, just like he used to in the old days – dear sweet chap. Then I pressed through the crowds of thousands of adoring, curious admirers who had all flocked here to welcome me. The brass bands dazzled me as I flounced ashore. I had finally arrived in the Promised Land.

America is simply a revelation. Manhattan is a blazing whirlwind of energy and optimism. New York really is a great and growing adolescent of a city, bursting all over with enthusiasm and charm. We transferred to the decadent splendour of the Albermarle Hotel, toured Central Park by carriage and dined at Delmonico's, the most famous restaurant in the city. Dear Oscar joined us that evening to trade a few bon mots with the crème de la crème of New York society. Millionaires and courtesans, stuffy New England squires and Wall Street bucks raised their glasses in unison to toast my health. The champagne flowed as freely as rain.

The dazzling lights of Broadway soon beckoned, for our play 'The Unequal Match' was about to steal a march on the Great White Way. After a frenzied week of rehearsals at Abbey's Park Theatre, our fabulous show was about to open. To lure in the punters, my name blazed in yellow electric lights right across the theatre roof. All was set fair for a spectacular opening.

I was reclining back at our hotel, powdering myself for dinner when our promoter rushed in with some shocking news. Disaster had struck! Our theatre was on fire! The newspapers joked later that it was the most expensive publicity stunt in history, but it truly was quite a shock. Undaunted by this setback, I cried out: "If my name escapes, I shall succeed. And if it burns, I shall still succeed". Well that great electric sign survived, like a good omen. We transferred down the road to Wallack's Theatre and our show went on to soar like a phoenix from the flames.

At the final curtain, the applause broke over me like a tidal wave. The crowds were rapturous, their response ecstatic. The newspaper reporters peppered me with question after question, prying and probing in that naïve yet impertinent American way. I met every one of their questions with my usual gay smile. The trick seemed to work.

The critics waxed lyrical about the Jersey Lily but spoke rather less effusively about the quality of the play. No matter. I always smile sweetly and never rise to the bait. It was the Prime Minister himself, William Gladstone, who once told me; "In your professional career, you will receive attacks, personal and critical, just and unjust. Bear them, never reply, and, above all, never rush into print to explain or defend yourself". He is right.

I simply adore America, with its unfurling horizons, the endless panoramas and sense of unending potential. Opportunity hangs in the air here like the promise of spring rain. Oscar and I took the train up to Niagara later for some publicity photographs. As he charmingly put it, they were taken with "the waterfall as a kind of unpretentious background". He is such a sweetie.

And of course I have fallen in love again. This time the lucky fellow is young Fred Gebhardt, a brash American bear of twenty-two, who by happy coincidence is heir to a stupendous fortune. Freddie is a connoisseur of the theatre world, a racehorse owner and above all a great admirer of feminine beauty. The press dub him the 'gilded youth', but he pursued me boldly with a determination well beyond his tender years. The poor dear is simply infatuated, like a doe-eyed young pup, and quite out of sympathy I allowed him into my boudoir. His energy and devotion have proved quite admirable.

Any lady of quality does her best to keep her lips sealed, and I will never speak to Freddie of the princes I have loved. The gossipmongers of the *Pink 'Un* will do their best of course to spread mischief, although the assiduous reach of the libel law is remarkably effective. Who can forget the *Town Talk* case, when some putrid little publisher was sent to two years in the brig for daring to spill a few beans?

I do hear from occasional stilted correspondence that my little 'niece', the fruit of one of my royal encounters, is growing up well back in Jersey. I am grateful to hear the news, but really cannot linger. I am dancing in the limelight of the New World and would rather brush the misfortunes of yesteryear into the wings. Life to me is a glorious banquet to drink and love and make merry and I have no time to entertain the shades of the past.

Young Freddie, though he will never know, would understand and accept these slightest blemishes on the Jersey Lily. He too is a man of strong passions and boundless ambition. And what Professional Beauty alive could resist the alluring spell of the heir to the throne? The Prince of Wales and I remain on cordial terms. Dear Bertie has of course moved on to pastures new, his roving eye unchecked even in his portly middle years. For my own part, I have found a new and more dramatic role to play.

It was the spell of one woman, the illustrious Sarah Bernhardt, which inspired my new career on the stage. Bernhardt is shockingly versatile and breathtakingly gifted, the finest character actress of this or any age. The 'Divine Sarah' is simply one of a kind. They say she sleeps in a velvet coffin and keeps a leopard-cub as a pet. Of course, Bertie was instantly besotted; her ravishing allure set even his jaded palate on fire. So I too resolved to take to the stage and prove to the world of men that I am so much more than a pretty face. I dare say I have already proved this in spades.

Last summer, I darted back to dingy old London to prise myself free from my dissolute, brandy-soaked husband. It is time to end this sham marriage. Yet the poor old fool blustered and demurred, so I have returned here to drink in once again the invigorating draught of the New World. Now Freddie and I are taking to the open railroad to conquer America.

We travel across the desert like Oriental kings. I insisted of course on a private railway car, seventy-five feet long, draped with solid silver fittings and padded in green silk brocade to guard my million-dollar visage against any unfortunate accident. We sweep the length and breadth of this immense continent, heading west towards the bright promise of California and raking in a king's ransom in every theatre and gambling den along the way.

We have christened our carriage 'Lalee', or 'Flirt', and this frisky name is emblazoned upon the royal blue livery, crowned of course by golden Jersey lilies. Lalee is my palace, my love-boat, my magnificent rolling boudoir. We boast guest rooms, staff quarters, even a saloon with a grand piano, where we can drink and dance until the small hours as we hurtle like a comet across the vastness of America.

When dear besotted Freddie opened his bulging purse, he really did spare no expense. We feast on whole stags, stored in the vast refrigerated compartments below decks. As the empty red desert rushes past, I draw my curtains of the finest Brussels lace and raise a toast again to my young and most generous lover. At remote Western stations, cowboys gaze awestruck as we pass and they doff their ten-gallon hats in my honour. I fend off marriage proposals from earnest Yankee braves almost every day.

My American tour is a riotous, sensational success. We are making money hand over fist, as if it were all just a glorious, madcap game. I always insist on the same dressing room layout; the same golden array of make-up and powder. Six thousand dollars a week flows in from each city and we spend it like water. Who knew it could all be so outrageously easy?

Somewhere, buried deep in my memory, I still remember the little stone vicarage in tiny, distant Jersey and the little child I left there. It feels like a faint echo from a distant world. The great steam engine sputters and screams as we roar along towards another destination. Lillie Langtry is coming to town, and millions across the continent will remember that name.

The desert skies above us are on fire. The Joshua trees, hands reaching out to heaven, are silhouetted in black against the bloody red sunset. Destiny is calling us further west, like pioneers caught up in the San Francisco gold rush. Tonight, Freddie and I will drink and whirl under the California stars. Tonight, I am the Queen of America.

A Lily in the Desert

*A*ll dreams come to an end. Oscar Wilde was thrown to the wolves, and in his hour of darkness, even his friend Lillie Langtry turned him aside. He died penniless and scorned in a decrepit Paris hotel. Only the judgment of history would restore him in due time to the pantheon of the greats.

For all her own scandals, the myth of Lillie Langtry continued to blaze brightly in the Victorian firmament. Her return to the Jersey Theatre Royal in 1891 was a triumph, and besotted crowds flocked to welcome their homecoming queen.

The grand love affair between Lillie and Freddie lasted for nine glorious and tempestuous years, but ended in disappointment. The California paradise they built together was cursed by ill fate, when a consignment of thoroughbred horses bound for their ranch was slaughtered in a freak railway accident. Lillie never visited her house again, and the estate was eventually sold. Meanwhile the brazenly cuckolded Mr Langtry, back in Victorian London, still refused to divorce his notoriously wayward spouse. Impatient and growing older, Freddie finally cashed in his chips and left the table.

America remained in the thrall of the Jersey Lily. Our story ends in an impossibly remote town, lost in the sunburned land and desiccated sagebrush of the Texas borderlands. In this harsh and alien land, half a world away from the lush fields and farms of Jersey, a strange shrine was raised in Lillie's honour. The town was named Langtry; whether by obscure coincidence, or by personal dedication as Lillie herself believed, no man could be entirely sure.

The local sheriff was the flamboyant Judge Roy Bean, an ebullient Justice of the Peace whose wits had half-scrambled in the heat of the Western sun. He was the self-proclaimed 'law west of the Pecos', dispensing summary judgment like a medieval king from his saloon bar porch. He handed out fines and sentences, clemency and favours, all delivered with a unique brand of homespun wisdom and jovial wisecracks.

On a rare trip back to civilisation, this eccentric yet charismatic sheriff chanced to see Lillie performing at a Chicago show, and thereafter, he worshipped her. 'King' Bean named his royal court the 'Jersey Lily Saloon' in her honour. He wrote to Lillie, begging her to come and visit. She politely declined but offered the town an ornamental drinking fountain as a gift. Immediately he telegraphed back that the only thing that the good folk of Langtry did not drink was water. So here on the western frontier, in this whisky-soaked, trigger-happy waterhole on the edge of the desert, a candle burned day and night for Jersey's greatest icon. And eventually, Lillie came.

It is 1904 in Langtry, Texas, when Lillie steps off the train. The Queen of America is surveying her court. A parade of leather-clad cowboys greet her in turn, followed in short order by the bejewelled 'beauties of Langtry' who curtsey and smile in turn as she descends. Her honour guard escort her to the shrine itself. The Jersey Lily saloon stands here in the empty desert like a strange relic, fallen from a distant star. Judge Bean is a few months' dead, but the entire town has turned out to greet their strange and glamorous icon. Like a queen presented with tribute from her people, the townspeople offer her a great cinnamon bear, growling and lashing before her on an iron chain. Before she can refuse, the beast throws off its shackles and scrambles away into the wilderness.

The townsfolk present her with Judge Bean's revolver, the symbol of his mortal power handed over to his icon of mortal beauty. The curious afternoon ends with a floral gift. Lillie is especially entranced by a box of resurrection plants, a resilient *desert survivor that can spring back into life after even the fiercest summer heat. They are a staple flower in this little town of Langtry.*

Then she waves goodbye, and the Desert Lily steams off towards the horizon, towards her glittering future, the hope of a better resurrection. As the train departs, a dust cloud swirls in a frenzy, then falls back to earth. The train is soon a vanishing smudge on the desert horizon and the dust settles back to rest on the empty tracks, as if it had never been.

Summer of the Mumming Birds

Jersey 1912

The Show Must Go On

*J*ersey's Scarlet Queen came home in the sultry July of 1900. The Opera House on Gloucester Street had recently burned to the ground in a shocking inferno. In true Victorian style, a new and immeasurably grander building had risen from the ashes like a phoenix. Its frontage still lay bare and unpainted but the first show could hardly wait. Who better to open this splendid new venue than the divine Jersey Lily herself?

The Victorian printing presses whirred breathlessly with a bevy of weasel words and titillating tales. Lillie's latest play, The Degenerates, dispensed another dose of scandal, for she played a courtesan who bathed in mud. Yet Lillie, ever a social climber, had now entered the leagues of minor aristocracy. As her fiftieth birthday loomed, she snapped up a dashing young baronet in his late twenties and duly assumed the unsuitably august title of 'Lady de Bathe'.

Naturally the incessant innuendo and gossip only inflamed Jersey's love for her wild and native Lily. The Degenerates proved a glorious triumph at the Opera House; huzzahs soared to the rafters and floral bouquets were hurled at the stage. Lillie rewarded her acolytes with a few gracious words of tribute to her home Island. Then she fled with the dawn.

It felt like the final flourish of a dying age. Within a year, Queen Victoria, the immense colossus that had towered over Great Britain, would finally fall. Generations had lived and died in the cloying comfort of her long shadow, but that age had now passed. A new and restless century had dawned. As the nineteenth century slipped away into the sepia realm of nostalgia, the old orthodoxies began to crumble. Working men dreamed of socialism; women demanded freedom. Ireland cried for Home Rule. The well-meaning New Liberal government in London seemed beset on all sides. The pole star of British supremacy was on the wane, as a young and rising Germany led an economic revolution. As its electrical and chemical industries boomed, it leapfrogged its former teacher. The new global power militarised rapidly. The new Empire was determined to seek its place in the sun, by any means necessary.

The world was changing fast, and the soporific peace of the Victorian age was coming to an end. On October 15, 1900, the Head Teachers of Jersey held a conference with their master, an Inspector Burrows. "He laid a great deal of stress on the importance of drill – military drill – for boys". One head proposed that 'a sergeant or other military man' be employed to teach drill, and his suggestion was enthusiastically endorsed. Jersey children were now being trained for war, the first harbinger of the age to come.

The Island slumbered fitfully on, secure in the gentle afterglow of Imperial hegemony and the security of a new entente cordiale with France. The coronation of Edward VII was celebrated across the globe in a blaze of Imperial glory, and Jersey inaugurated its own lavish floral parade to mark the event. They dubbed it the Battle of Flowers.

The Opera House itself flourished. Its gilded theatre resounded weekly to the applause of the smug and contented Jersey bourgeoisie, revelling in the pleasant cultural life of an Island that had changed beyond recognition over Victoria's long and eventful watch. Now the comfortable classes sought to cling to the waning days of Britain's Indian summer, even as the colder nights drew in.

So it was that one damp and dreary August day, Fred Karno's roving troupe of japers and pranksters washed up on Jersey's shores. They had come straight from a gruelling American tour. One of the jokers in the pack was a young south London lad of twenty-three, whose blue eyes had already born witness to a lifetime of sorrows. Of course no one knew his name. He was just another promising young clown treading the boards, earning a crust, holding on for tomorrow.

As it happens, he was called Charles. He bore his father's name.

The Clown's Story – Charlie Chaplin

Jersey Opera House, August 1912

The music hall was my mother's meat and my father's drink. They say parents live on through their children, and today the show must go on. As a boy I stalked like a ghost along the streets of London, squinting in through the blackened and frosted windows. A grinding, maddening hunger consumed me, for I had scarcely eaten in days. I sidled past the soft and gentle lights of restaurants, where happy families smiled and feasted. I gawped at the soft velvet clothes of respectable men, dazzled by the flash of their gold sovereigns, as if they were elegant creatures from another world. I feel that I have always spent my life on the outside, slowly freezing in the icy midwinter, peering in through a wall of glass.

I remember the father who betrayed us all; his mind blinded by the bottle, a man who burned his liver out along with his music hall career before he was thirty. Charles Chaplin Senior walked out on his children and soon drank himself into a pauper's grave, following the well-worn path from the vanity fair of the Kennington stage to the dull oblivion of the Horns Tavern. My beautiful, devoted mother once sang like an angel, but her beauty and spirit would not save her. One day Fate stole her pretty voice, and she would never sing again. She was a caged bird, struck dumb, her wings broken. She was jeered off-stage. So we soon sank down from our threadbare respectability and plummeted down the slope into the abyss. The maelstrom inevitably dragged us under, a downward spiral of debts and bailiffs and despair. A bitter, gnawing hunger riled me day and night. I had never realised just how low men and women can fall.

Life proved to be a cruel taskmaster. My father was dead. My poor mother was imprisoned in Cane Hill Lunatic Asylum, her mind broken. This pitiless world saw us as the scum of the earth, human refuse to be buried without trace. I was soon a pariah, a booby-hatch boy, my head shaved and doused in iodine for ringworm. I felt like a leper. I remember the utter desolation of the workhouse, when we little infants sang 'Abide with me' as the black night fell down like a shroud over Victorian London. Sadness welled deep in our hearts, for we were utterly alone, and these were evil days. One day, I was hauled to the stage in front of an audience of hundreds, and sentenced like a criminal for the sins of another. I remember the vicious bite of the workhouse birch, and feeling absolutely nothing, for I was already numb on the inside. I was a hollow child, a ghost stalking an empty world.

In time I graduated from this pit of hell, and was released back onto the streets.

In desperation, and fondly recalling my mother's lost music hall career, I lodged my particulars with a theatre company on the Strand. I expected nothing and hoped for nothing. I took on hard labour to keep the hunger at bay. I merely willed to survive, to carry on with the show.

One day, I was chopping wood for money, hacking and burning away my own past, when the casting call came. My golden ticket away from destitution had finally come good. So I worked until I dropped, rehearsed my act to the point of exhaustion, and mastered my craft. Today I travel the length and breadth of the kingdom as a leading clown in Fred Karno's celebrated company, draped in vaudeville stage glamour, bringing mirth to thousands in a travelling troupe. Our busy schedule this year has brought us to the Opera House on this lovely little isle of Jersey.

They say history repeats itself first as tragedy, and then as farce. So tonight I am playing my own father. I am playing the Inebriated Swell, a pie-eyed buffoon, slave to the bottle and a bundle of laughs. The play is an outrageous, uproarious send-off of the English music hall tradition, where my beloved mother once frolicked on the sad road to the asylum. Our show is called *Mumming Birds*, and the Jersey press is already declaring it a theatrical triumph.

As I shamble drunkenly into my stage box, even my eccentric gait draws titters and whoops of delight. So I prance and prattle for their pleasure, peeling my gloves off, tipping an attendant then trying in vain to remove my glove again from my bare skin. The Saucy Soubrette sings a ditty in my ear, like a mother soothing her child. I hurl down vegetables at the other actors, lampooning their artistic pretensions as they pretend to perform a show. Having dismally failed to light my cigar by electric light, I stretch dangerously out of my box to reach for a match, teetering in exaggerated fashion on the edge of the abyss.

Suddenly, I fall. This little manoeuvre takes practice, but after all, I have form. So I plunge down, exploding like a bomb onto the stage. The pantomime music hall show collapses in confusion and the audience roars its delight like the swell on the bay. I duly doff my hat and bow. Jersey Opera House shakes to its foundations with the rapturous thunder of applause.

Beyond the piercing glare of the footlights, I can glimpse them all: little children in hysterics, portly respectable ladies whooping uncontrollably, fine gentlemen choking on their chortles like a leg of mutton. The comfortable classes of Jersey have been mesmerised by this lost workhouse boy. I drink in the applause, as heart-warming as a shot of the local Calvados, as addictive as a dose of opium. Their faces bray and snort in delight, mirth rippling over their bewhiskered lips and their quivering double chins. A rogue thought leaps into my jester's mind. I am a fool, for the sake of my show. Whose fool are you?

I sleep late the next day. Pretty little Jersey feels a world away from the dazzling metropolitan theatres, or the drinking pits of south London. The air here is salt-heavy and beguiling, reminding me of one lost boyhood day, before the fall, when we joyously dipped our toes in the sea at Southend-on-Sea. I never saw the sea again as a child. St Helier is even more delightful, though for all its French airs it is branded with all the hallmarks of British provincialism. A grand statue of Queen Victoria dominates the Weighbridge, her heavy shadow still hanging like an implacable burden over our age. Little engines trundle out from the nearby railway station, creeping westwards along the arc of the bay. The wooden warehouses that line the Esplanade are packed high in season with potatoes for export for the finest markets in London.

Tomorrow is the climax of the Battle of Flowers, a charming parade that since the late King Edward's coronation has formed the mainstay of the summer season here. The weather has been rather foul in these parts of late, but we can hardly miss the chance to take part in such a celebration. At a loose end that afternoon, my cast members and I join the parade on Victoria Avenue, marching in unison as a theatre troupe to amuse the crowds of assorted onlookers and good-timers.

They are still putting the finishing touches to the Battle displays, great floral barges, lavish flower-sacrifices to the gods of fate and summer and chance. I prance past the floats in character, drolly reprising my role as the tipsy music hall buffoon. The people love it. I break out from the line and perform an impromptu performance. Staggering past, clowning and japing it up to high heaven, I draw titters and cheers from the audience. I drink in the applause.

Out of the corner of my eye, a man is cranking up one of those curious new-fangled marvels, a cinematographic camera for taking motion pictures. I am told he has come down from London for the purpose, at the behest of the *Topical Gazette*, and is grinding his machine for all its worth. Almost as many people seem to be watching him as me. I love novelty, and this is my first time on film, but it seems to fit me like a glove. The crowds roar out their acclaim, and the sea air is fresh with the scent of opportunity.

My little solo escapade is coming to an end. I bow jauntily and revel in the cheers. Just as I saunter back into the mêlée, I spy a little boy, his face dirty and smudged, gazing at me with pure adoration. I look back at him and see myself. He is a grimy street urchin, dirty but clinging to his pride, entranced by the show. The boy calls out to a distant mother, "Oh mamma, why has he gone away? I did want to see the funny man again?" His laughter burns in my ears like a promise.

In that moment, I begin to understand. This is the shape of things to come. The cine-camera whirrs and turns, spinning out my future. Suddenly the sun breaks in

[""]

through the cloudbank high over St Aubin's Bay, and hangs above the horizon like a glorious sign. The 1912 Battle of Flowers glides on. The little lost boy turns and smiles at me for one last time, before he is swallowed up by the carnival. I slip back into the warm embrace of the parade, my ears ringing with his laughter, dancing on towards tomorrow.

The Butterfly

The Battle of Flowers changed everything. Chaplin looked at once for a chance to break into the intoxicating and fledgling world of celluloid film. First, the vistas of an American vaudeville tour beckoned. Within eighteen months of wowing the crowd at the Jersey Opera House, the cloudburst of fame broke open. The West Coast producer Mack Sennett watched the acclaimed Mumming Birds show, smelt raw talent, and immediately signed Chaplin up to Keystone Pictures. Soon the horizons of California unfurled in an endless paradise of orange groves and ocean blue and shimmering sunshine.

One day, in a drab prop hut in a Hollywood field, Chaplin spontaneously grabbed an eclectic collection of props. The magic took mere seconds. Like a glorious butterfly emerging from its chrysalis, the Little Tramp was born. Soon his name was flashing in bold electric lights on Times Square: "Chaplin signs with Mutual at six hundred and seventy thousand a year".

Suddenly the workhouse boy is a millionaire, as if the dregs of the earth are now hailed as its finest wine. Chaplin is proclaimed a genius, and his Hollywood confidante is Jersey's very own scarlet novelist, Mrs Elinor Glyn, whose slushy romances lure millions to the box office. Chaplin's future blazes as bright and dazzling as the burning white arcs of the studio Klieg lamps.

Half a world away from Hollywood Boulevard, the bedraggled and limpid cabbage trees sway like poor man's palms over Jersey's Victoria Avenue, lashed by the blustery squalls of the British summer. They can stand proud, for this is where the path to immortality first began.

121

Finale: Last Days of August

Jersey, August 26, 1912

Hydro-Aeroplane Races, St Aubin's Bay

August 26, 1912

Let the glorious kaleidoscope turn! The last days of August 1912 are passing now, hurtling away in a whirlwind of light. The *Mumming Birds* have already taken wing and their fledgling star, Charlie Chaplin, has left Jersey and set sail for immortality. Change hangs fresh in the air, as pungent as the *vraic* churned up every day by the angry tides.

As August rolls on, the miracles have fallen thicker and faster. Today, the gossamer prophets of the new world descended from heaven in their fantastical, hummingbird machines. The first Aviators whipped up a jubilant frenzy today on the sands of St Aubin's Bay. The crowds surged and cheered, as the good folk of old Jersey caught an electric glimpse of a shocking tomorrow.

Evening is closing in now. Miss Adderson, that brash young woman who brought fresh coffee to the first airmen, has just retired to Bay View Terrace to enjoy a last cup of cocoa before bedtime. Her mind racing with the excitement of the day, she dreams softly of Jersey as the red sun slinks lower in the sky. She conjures up the voices of Jersey's past, whispering to her of forgotten things, confiding all their hidden histories.

Beyond, the Jersey tides roll in across the bay, as they always have done. They care nothing for little tramps or heroic pilots. Here in this slimy moonscape where Helier crouched on his rock, where King Charles sheltered in his castle, the sea and land tussle as ever in their daily pantomime struggle. But their battle is now in vain, for something changed forever when the Aviators descended from the skies. Today the prison walls of the Island exploded. The sea will no longer be Jersey's gaoler, for the sky itself has fallen before the vaulting ambition of men.

The dissipating Jersey crowds drift home, still mesmerised by the astonishing spectacle of those flying machines that descended from heaven and have now soared back up to it again. Now only the fat white gulls wheel in the untamed skies beyond, their paths as obscure and arcane as the motion of the clouds. They are no longer its masters.

As Jean Benoist and his fellow Aviators ascend back to heaven, the milling spectators are mere black ants, an indistinct and heaving swarm far beneath them. The crowd on the beach is a mere scuttling shadow now, washed along by the tide, fated to be swept away who knows where? The pilots spy a brace of horse traps and a few motor landaus tumbling like stones along the length of Victoria Avenue, until the road itself peters out in the sand dunes before St Peter's Marsh. The bay beyond them stretches into eternity. They soar over the semi-derelict infant school and the undecorated and bland chapel of St Matthew's, as yet untouched by the miracle of glass. Yet the Aviators are lost in the jostle for racing positions and prizes, caught in a world of vertiginous altitude and technical calibrations, and have little time to appreciate the magnificent panorama unfolding below.

Far below, the little kingdom of Jersey is receding far away, as if it is a great green pebble lodged in the rapids. Leave behind the brute, brooding symmetry of the Fort ramparts and the thick gaggle of grey Town streets and crescents. Leave behind the Esplanade, where the potato warehouses lie black and empty, and the tide will soon race in to lash the sea wall. The cluster of jagged rocks at La Collette tumble down into the sea, shattered like broken glass.

Leave behind the grand Jersey mansions, with the splendid arboretums and manicured gardens, where the wealthy survey their starched little empires. Dark-clad servants scrub and dust immaculate drawing rooms, glancing up for a moment as the alarming and novel whine of the aeroplane drones overhead. Leave behind the redbrick coastal villas where the petty potentates of Empire have wound up 'on the beach', their eyes still asquint from their ruddy days in the equatorial sun. Leave behind the marching rows of little schoolchildren all trussed up like sailors, and the black perambulators bringing the babies home.

Seen from the skies, the spindly steam railways seem to snake out from the old town like arteries, weaving west from Weighbridge Station and skirting east from Snow Hill, past the thick swamps of Les Marais, heading out for the terminus at Gorey Pier. The great Castle looms large; still unbowed. Closer to hand, the decaying Gothic dagger of the Prince's Tower juts up prominently as the Island's greatest landmark. It looms over the pristine land where a young Victoria once rode, half an age ago.

In the windswept west, the British Army Barracks stand as bold and proud as the British Empire, perched on St Peter's grassy and desolate plain. Perhaps one day in the future, flying machines might find this great plateau a convenient landing ground. Time will tell. The firing ranges up here are all too busy these days, as the nation girds itself for the shadow of a darker future. Then the hydroplanes wheel away, and the dark horizon of the Continent soon looms into view. The Aviators vanish into the sunset.

August has been a month to remember. The Little Tramp who clowned at the Opera House this month will soon be setting sail for America, and within two years he will have taken Hollywood by storm. Other young actors are already lurking in the wings, waiting for the twentieth century to call them on stage.

Born within four days of Chaplin, another moustachioed young man is drifting this month like a tramp around the streets of Vienna. One day, Chaplin will lampoon him on screen as the 'Great Dictator'. But in this summer of 1912, he is simply an aggrieved young man, yet another failed artist, waiting for his luck to turn.

His luck will turn. The whole world seems as if it is chafing at the leash this summer, waiting for tomorrow to happen. The lights are burning late these days in the courts and chancelleries of Europe; the talk is of opening gambits and the inexorable logic of munitions schedules and railway timetables. In the complex and perfidious chess game of the Great Powers, too many now believe that only he who plays the opening move will win.

Some are already darkly hinting that Europe needs to be swept, as if by an iron broom. These days, the newsflashes reach a somnolent Jersey as telegraphs from a darker, more foreboding world. The Jersey press faithfully reports the latest "Flashes by wire", a dismal litany of worsening news from across a restless, seething Continent. "The Balkan situation: Serbs in Danger", reads the latest alarmist headline. There are fearsome reports of terrorist outrages in the perennial powder kegs of Bosnia and Serbia. Meanwhile, British diplomats have just departed from yet another failed peace conference in Russia, held "between the groups of powers ceaselessly arming against one another".

Turn the page to domestic news. Reports filter in from a Eugenics conference in London, where speaker after speaker denounces the "problem of the unfit". "Eugenics may seem a cold-blooded scientific morality; but on the other hand, we must never forget that hard discipline is necessary if the nation is to be virile". The serpent of the twentieth century is already in the garden. Turn the page. "Do your children like cakes and buns and little tarts?" gently enquires a cherubic little advertisement. Time to smile awhile and lose yourself in hearty tales of flying machines and absurd music-hall farce.

So now the last days of the summer of 1912 are flashing by like a Jersey train and leaving only memories: of milk stout in the pubs; of the Inebriated Swell who gaily stormed the Opera House; of wars fought only with flowers; of brave Aviators who plunged down from heaven like a glorious sign.

Leave behind the young Jersey ladies intoxicated with romance, dreaming of a love that lasts forever, but destined to be widows by twenty-five. Leave behind the dashing Jersey boys, fresh with the first bloom of youth, yet already entering the twilight years of their brutally truncated lives. To paraphrase the young radical Mr Trotsky, they may not have been interested in war, but war was most definitely interested in them. The twentieth century was coming for Jersey, and each one of its bloody promises would be fulfilled in due time.

It is nightfall over Jersey and the Aviators have soared away. The last of the Mumming Birds have flown. At journey's end, the beautiful rays of sunset fall over the ancient fields of Jersey, over the dolmens from the distant past, the square where Jersey won its freedom, and the peaceful green valley where Queen Victoria once rode. After her, the flood would come.

Summer's day now is done. The bloody, trembling sun plunges like a knife into the ocean, setting the horizon on fire. Its fleeting beauty fades to black, leaving only a brace of ghost clouds ruffling gently under the cold moon.

In Helier's ancient church, the candles still burn, shining against the gathering night, guiding the lost travellers of the huddled ages home. The stained glass hangs in the darkness here like a night rainbow, a glimmering fragment of memory. These walls remember. They stand heavy with the weight of their hidden histories.

Night has fallen, and Jersey slips away into its summer dreams. Then the tide turns, unseen. In the depths of the bay beyond, the black floodwater sweeps up towards the silent shore.

THE END

Acknowledgments

I would like to acknowledge the invaluable encouragement of my father-in-law Graham, the helpfulness of the staff at Jersey Library, and above all the unfailing support of my wife and my family. I am very grateful to my aunt Dawn for reviewing the final manuscript. I especially thank my parents and teachers for encouraging my early love of history. Three decades later, I hope you enjoy reading this book.

About the Author

The author was born in Surrey in 1976 and now lives in Jersey. He was educated at the Royal Grammar School, Guildford and holds a First in Modern History from St Hugh's College, Oxford. *Jersey: The Hidden Histories* is his first book.

Uniform with the present volume, JERSEY: THE HIDDEN HISTORIES:

The story of Jersey is shaped by the sea. The treacherous Channel waters drowned the King of England's son in the White Ship and plunged his realm into chaos. Jersey legends tell of the waves that swept away the doomed manor of La Brecquette and sprung the fearsome trap of the Golden Chair.

Yet the ocean's call of adventure inspired the mariners of Jersey to traverse the world. It tempted Sir Walter Raleigh, Jersey's fallen Governor, into his fatal quest for El Dorado, and drove local boy Tom Davis to build a fortune in Africa. The same pioneering spirit led Lilian Grandin, Jersey's first female doctor, to set sail for China, where she would sacrifice her life.

Jersey: Secrets of the Sea is their story, imagined in their own words. Step onto the bridge of RMS *Titanic* with her Jersey quartermaster just as the deadly iceberg looms into view, while Islander Lucy Duff-Gordon slumbers in her first-class suite below. Discover the story of her sister Elinor Glyn, who found fame at the peak of Hollywood's Golden Age.

Stand with the Jersey Company volunteers as they leave St Helier for the Great War; and watch the lone boatman in 1941 slipping away from the shadow of the German Occupation.

Jersey: Secrets of the Sea is the panoramic story of an Island forged by the seas, set at the crossroads of maritime history, and told through the voices of the Jersey seafarers who made it.

~

'With the maritime theme as a link between chapters, this warmly welcomed follow-up to his *Jersey: The Hidden Histories* once again takes a selection of characters from history and legend and retells their stories.... This salty landfall of merchants, smugglers, fisherfolk, privateers and explorers owes a debt of gratitude to Paul Darroch for so entertainingly recounting how Jersey became what it is' – from a review in the *Jersey Evening Post*

Complete list of Seaflower Books, 2022 ~

BLAME THE BADGER by Mike Stentiford OBE	£6.95
CHANNEL FISH by Marguerite Paul	£11.95
CHEERS! DRINKS AND DRINKING IN JERSEY by Alasdair Crosby	£9.95
EXOTIC GARDEN PLANTS IN THE CHANNEL ISLANDS by Janine Le Pivert	£9.95
A FARMER'S VACATION IN 1873 by George E Waring	£5.00
GUERNSEY COUNTRY DIARY by Nigel Jee	£4.95
ISLAND KITCHEN by Marguerite Paul	£11.95
JERSEY HORSES FROM THE PAST by John Jean	£4.95
JERSEY IN LONDON by Brian Ahier Read	£6.95
JERSEY JAUNTS by John Le Dain	£6.95
THE JERSEY LILY by Sonia Hillsdon	£6.95
JERSEY OCCUPATION DIARY by Nan Le Ruez	£11.95
JERSEY RAMBLES by John Le Dain	£6.95
JERSEY: SECRETS OF THE SEA by Paul Darroch	£11.95
JERSEY WAR WALKS by Ian Ronayne	£8.95
JERSEY WEATHER AND TIDES by Peter Manton	£5.95
JOHN SKINNER'S VISIT TO THE CHANNEL ISLANDS: August 1827	£2.50
JOURNEY ROUND ST HELIER by Robin Pittman	£7.95
LIFE ON SARK by Jennifer Cochrane	£5.95
MINED WHERE YOU WALK by Richard Le Tissier	£6.95
PHILIP DE CARTERET R.N. by Jane Ashelford	£9.95
THE OTHER JERSEY BOYS by Davd Knight	£9.95
THE POOR SHALL INHERIT Daff Noel	£6.95
PROMISES NOT FORGOTTEN by Gerald Breen	£11.95
WILD ISLAND by Peter Double	£7.95
WILDLIFE OF THE CHANNEL ISLANDS by Sue Daly	£14.95
WISH YOU WERE HERE by John Le Dain	£7.95

Please visit our website for more details
SEAFLOWER BOOKS may be ordered through our website using Paypal
We send books post-free within the UK and Channel Islands
SEAFLOWER BOOKS are also available via your local bookshop or from Amazon

SEAFLOWER BOOKS
www.ex-librisbooks.co.uk